THE MODERN LIBRARY
OF THE WORLD'S BEST BOOKS

THE BEST OF S. J. PERELMAN

The publishers will be pleased to send, upon request, an illustrated folder setting forth the purpose and scope of THE MODERN LIBRARY, *and listing each volume in the series. Every reader of books will find titles he has been looking for, handsomely printed, in definitive editions, and at an unusually low price.*

THE BEST OF

S. J. PERELMAN

With a Critical Introduction by

SIDNEY NAMLEREP

**THE
MODERN LIBRARY
NEW YORK**

Acknowledgments are due *The New Yorker*, in which most of these stories first appeared, and *College Humor*, *Judge*, *Life*, *Contact* and *Stage Magazine* for permission to reprint material which was first published in their pages.

Published in New York by Random House, Inc. and simultaneously in Toronto, Canada, by Random House of Canada, Ltd., 1947

Random House IS THE PUBLISHER OF

THE MODERN LIBRARY

BENNETT A. CERF · DONALD S. KLOPFER · ROBERT K. HAAS

Manufactured in the United States of America

By H. Wolff

TO ROBERT C. BENCHLEY

TABLE OF CONTENTS

Contents

INTRODUCTION

In any consideration of S. J. Perelman—and S. J. Perelman certainly deserves the same consideration one accords old ladies on street cars, babies traveling unescorted on planes, and the feeble-minded generally—it is important to remember the crushing, the well-nigh intolerable odds under which the man has struggled to produce what may well be, in the verdict of history, the most picayune prose ever produced in America. Denied every advantage, beset and plagued by ill fortune and a disposition so crabbed as to make Alexander Pope and Dr. Johnson seem sunny by contrast, he has nevertheless managed to belt out a series of books each less distinguished than its predecessor, each a milestone of bombast, conceit, pedantry, and strutting pomposity. In his pages proliferate all the weird grammatical flora tabulated by H. W. Fowler in his *Modern English Usage*—the Elegant Variation, the Facetious Zeugma, the Cast-Iron Idiom, the Battered Ornament, the Bower's-Bird Phrase, the Sturdy Indefensible, the Side-Slip, and the Unequal Yokefellow. His work is a museum of mediocrity, a monument to the truly banal. What Flaubert did to the French bourgeois in *Bouvard and Pecuchet*, what Pizarro did to the Incas, what Jack Dempsey did to Paolino Uzcudun, S. J. Perelman has done to American belles-lettres.

It is customary to palliate the shortcomings of certain eminent men by pleading their physical drawbacks. Dostoievsky's epilepsy, Beethoven's deafness and Milton's blindness have all been served up on occasion to explain their vagaries. The same must be done for S. J. Perelman, except that he has labored under a far greater handicap. Extraordinary though it may seem, his entire output over the past two decades has been achieved without benefit of brain. The plain medical fact which cannot be blinked (and if we are to blink it, we must accept the consequences) is that his skull is little more than a hollow gourd, a mere bony knob on which reposes a battered Herbert Johnson hat. How he contrives to fulfil the ordinary obligations of everyday life—to get to his office, philander with his secretary, bedevil his wife, and terrorize his children—is one of those mysteries of science like the common cold or mixed bathing. The rest of his physique is even less prepossessing. Under a forehead roughly comparable to that of the Javanese or the Piltdown Man are visible a pair of tiny pig eyes, lit up alternately by greed and concupiscence. His nose, broken in childhood by a self-inflicted blow with a hockey stick, has a prehensile tip, ever quick to smell out an insult; at the least suspicion of an affront, Perelman, who has the pride of a Spanish grandee, has been known to whip out his sword-cane and hide in the nearest closet. He has a good figure, if not a spectacular one; above the hips, a barrel chest and a barrel belly form a single plastic unit which bobbles uncertainly on a pair of skinny shanks. In motion, the man's body may best be likened to a New Bedford whaler in the teeth of an equinoctial gale; in repose, it is strongly reminiscent of a giant sloth. In point of fact, from what small exterior evidence we possess, it would appear that he has modeled himself closely on that luckless animal. A monstrous indolence, cheek by jowl with the kind of irascibility displayed by a Vermont postmaster while sorting the morning mail, is perhaps his chief characteristic. Small wonder that he should have chosen for his book-plate that significant Revolutionary emblem, a crouched rattlesnake above the terse injunction, "Don't Tread on Me."

But these idiosyncrasies, however striking, bear no more reference to Perelman's work than Landru's social graces did to his. Really to comprehend his writing (a project on a par with understanding Chichen-itza), one should examine random passages. Let us select a few instances and explore, without rancor, their sources and implications. Take, for example, the two sentences in the essay called "Kitchen Bouquet" which opens this volume. The author is speaking of a servant he employed briefly one summer: "For some reason I never could fathom, unless it was that I occasionally wore a Tattersall vest, William persisted in regarding me as a racing man. He could recall every entry in the Cesarewitch Sweepstakes since 1899 and did, but faced with a pot roast, he assumed a wooden incomprehension that would have done credit to a Digger Indian." Now, although Perelman deliberately disavows any knowledge of racing, the references to the Tattersall vest and the Cesarewitch Sweepstakes mark him as an habitué of the tracks. Yet it can be stated with absolute authority that his closest contact with horse-hair was a short snooze on a Victorian sofa in 1916. The actual origin of these allusions was as follows. Some twenty-four years ago, he borrowed and wore to a junior tea-dance at his university a Tattersall vest, a circumstance which apparently impressed itself on the snobbish adolescent mind. Ten years later, in the English Bar at Chantilly, he overheard two elderly jockeys heatedly discussing the Cesarewitch. It was therefore inevitable that, since Perelman suffers from what psychologists euphemistically term total recall, he should have dredged up these references when the opportunity arose. Anyone with a primitive sense of decency would have hesitated to exhume them, but this scavenger, this literary ghoul whose exploits would horrify a Scottish medical school, sticks at nothing. With fiendish nonchalance and a complete lack of reverence for good form, he plucks words out of context, ravishes them, and makes off whistling as his victims sob brokenly into the bolster.

But it is when the reader comes face to face with a gigantic kitchen midden like "Scenario," the eleventh article in this collection, that his imagination reels. What is one to say of such deplorable lapses of logic and decorum as "Gentlemen, I give you Martha Custis, hetman of the Don Cossacks, her features etched with the fragile beauty of a cameo" or "It's midsummer madness, Fiametta! You mustn't! I must! I want you! You want me? But I—I'm just a poor little slavey, and you—why, all life's ahead of you! Fame, the love of a good woman, children! And your music, Raoul! Excuse me, miss, are you Fiametta Desplains? I am Yankel Patchouli, a solicitor. Here is my card and a report of my recent urinalysis. Raoul! Raoul! Come quick! A million dollars! Now you can go to Paris and study your counterpoint! Damn my music, Fiametta, my happiness was in my own back yard all the time and I was, how you say it, one blind fool." It is all very well to condone Perelman on the ground that he wrote the foregoing after extended servitude in Hollywood, but what if such passages were to fall into the hands of children? Particularly children who did not know the meaning of words like "patchouli"?

Unquestionably, the two most dominant themes in the ensuing pages, if any general pattern can be discerned, are those relating to money and women. Again and again Perelman's quenchless preoccupation with moola and the female figure invades his discourses; a cursory inspection reveals thirty-seven direct allusions to the former and twenty-four to the latter. Some of the articles ("Adorable, Taxable You" and "Farewell, My Lovely Appetizer") actually deal with nothing else; and this lamentable undertone of avarice and lubricity probably reaches its zenith in "You Should Live So, Walden Pond" with the phrase, "Hardly am I back in the Taj Mahal, surrounded by Madeleine Carroll and five hundred million billion trillion dollars." Obvious infantilism of this sort can be forgiven a gifted writer; in one so patently devoid of talent as Perelman, his continual absorption with the fleshpots indicates the need for speedy therapy. Either he should set his sights for Miss Carroll and her bankroll or betake himself to that good five-cent psychiatrist he is forever prating about.

For it is evident to anyone with a grain of sense and the price of this volume (on which Perelman, unfortunately, received a stipulated royalty) that the man faces a disastrous future. With luck, he may end his days stretched out on a luxurious ottoman, surrounded by swarms of luscious fawn-eyed bayaderes feeding him sweetmeats. Without, he may wind up on a similar couch, listlessly intoning his dreams to a rather bored Viennese at twenty-five dollars an hour. Whatever happens, the damage he has done to the language is incalculable. Like Attila's horse, of whom it was said that grass would never grow again where once it trod, Perelman leaves behind him a spoor of crushed and bleeding prose that will never flower again. A plague on all his grouses!

1626 Broadway   Sidney Namlerep
New York City

THE BEST
OF
S. J.
PERELMAN

KITCHEN BOUQUET

Yesterday morning I awoke from a deep dream of peace compounded of equal parts of allonal and Vat 69 to find that autumn was indeed here. The last leaf had fluttered off the sycamore and the last domestic of the summer solstice had packed her bindle and caught the milk train out of Trenton. Peace to her ashes, which I shall carry up henceforward from the cellar. Stay as sweet as you are, honey, and don't drive through any open drawbridges is my Christmas wish for Leota Claflin. And lest the National Labor Relations Board (just plain "Nat" to its friends, of whom I am one of the staunchest) summon me to the hustings for unfair employer tactics, I rise to offer in evidence as pretty a nosegay of houseworkers as ever fried a tenderloin steak. Needless to say, the characters and events depicted herein are purely imaginary, and I am a man who looks like Ronald Colman and dances like Fred Astaire.

The first reckless crocus of March was nosing up through the lawn as I sprang from the driver's seat, spread my cloak across a muddy spot, and obsequiously handed down Philomène Labruyère—colored, no laundry. Philomène was a dainty thing, built somewhat on the order of Lois De Fee, the lady bouncer. She had the rippling muscles of a panther, the stolidity of a water buffalo, and the lazy insolence of a shoe salesman. She stood seventy-five inches in her stocking feet, which I will take my Bible oath were prehensile. As she bent down to lift her suitcase,

3

she picked up the car by mistake and had it halfway down the slope before I pointed out her mistake. She acknowledged the reproof with a glance of such sheer hatred that I knew at once I should have kept my lip buttoned. After all, perhaps the woman wanted my automobile in her bedroom for some purpose of her own.

"You—you can take it up with you if you want," I stammered, thinking to retrieve her esteem. "I've got plenty of others—I mean I've got plenty of nothing—I mean—" With my ears glowing, I attempted to conceal my gaffe by humming a few bars of "Summertime," but her cold, appraising glance told me that Philomène had me pegged.

"Whuh kine place is this?" she rumbled suspiciously. "You mus' be crazy."

"But aren't we all?" I reminded her with a charming smile. "C'est la maladie du temps—the sickness of the times—don't you think? Fin-de-siècle and lost generation, in a way. 'I should have been a pair of ragged claws scuttling across the floors of silent seas.' How well Eliot puts it! D'ye ever see any of the old transition crowd?" I skipped along doing my best to lighten her mood, carried her several hatboxes, and even proffered a reefer, but there was no doubt in either of our minds who had the upper hand.

That Philomène was a manic-depressive in the downhill phase was, of course, instantly apparent to a boy of five. Several boys of five, who happened to be standing around and were by way of being students of psychopathology, stated their belief to me in just those words:

4

"Manic-depressive, downhill phase." At the close of business every evening, Philomène retired to her room armed with a sixteen-inch steak knife, doubtless to ward off an attack by her Poltergeist. She then spent the best part of an hour barricading her door with dressers, armoires, and other heavy furniture, preparatory to sleeping with the lights on. I say "sleeping" utterly without conviction; she undoubtedly molded lead statues of her employer and crooned to them over a slow fire.

But if her behavior was erratic, there was no lack of consistency in Philomène's cuisine. Meat loaf and cold fried chicken succeeded each other with the deadly precision of tracer bullets. At last, when blood and sinew could stand no more and I was about to dissolve the union, I suddenly discovered that this female Paul Bunyan had grown to womanhood under the bright skies of Martinique, and I knew a moment of elation. I let it be bruited through the servants' hall that I would look tolerantly on fried plantain, yams, and succulent rice dishes. That afternoon the kitchen was a hive of activity. The air was heavy with saffron, pimento, and allspice. I heard snatches of West Indian Calypsos, caught a glimpse of Philomène's head swathed in a gay bandanna. With the care befitting a special occasion, I dressed negligently but with unimpeachable taste in whites and cummerbund, mixed myself several excellent stengahs, and sauntered in to dinner for all the world like an up-country tea planter. A few moments later, Philomène entered with what might be called a smoking salver except for the circumstance that it was stone cold. On it lay the wing and undercarriage of an even colder chicken, flanked by two segments of meat loaf.

After five minutes of reflection, during which, I am told, my features closely resembled a Japanese print, I arose and, throwing out my tiny chest, marched into the kitchen. The maledictions withered on my lips. Seated at the table, my black hibiscus blossom was tucking in a meal consisting of *potage Parmentier avec croûtons*, a crisp *gigot, salade fatiguée*, and *pot de crème au chocolat*.

"You—thing," I said at length, and five minutes later Philomène was on her way back to St. Pierre.

Her successor was a chapfallen Australian cadaver who had reached his zenith as steward of a country club in Pompton Lakes and treated me and mine with the tired fatalism of a social worker. For some reason I never could fathom, unless it was that I occasionally wore a Tattersall vest, William persisted in regarding me as a racing man. He could recall every entry in the Cesarewitch Sweepstakes since 1899 and did, but faced with a pot roast, he assumed a wooden incomprehension that would have done credit to a Digger Indian. It was William's opinion, freely given, that cooked food was dead food and that I would triple my energy by living on fronds. He knew a hundred different ways of preparing bran, each more ghastly than the last. For an avowed vegetarian (or "raw-fooder," as he described himself), he spent his leisure in a puzzling enough fashion, polishing and whetting the superb collection of Swedish steel carving knives which was the one relic of his former magnificence.

William hadn't been with us long before I began to

feel uneasy, but I attributed my disquiet to Edmund Pearson's admirable study of the Lizzie Borden case, which I was reading at the time. And then, on the sultry morning of August 4th—by an uncanny coincidence the forty-seventh anniversary of the Fall River holocaust—I came down to find awaiting me an exact duplicate of the breakfast which had been served on Second Street that fateful morning: warmed-over mutton soup, cold mutton, and bananas. I am not unduly superstitious, but there is no sense flying in the face of history. I left the check and the usual reference on William's bureau and hid in the woods until traintime.

The time had now come, I felt, for plain speaking. I inserted two and a half inches in the metropolitan press setting forth my special needs. I wanted something stout and motherly, with floury hands and a hot apple pie cooling on the window sill. What I got was an ancient Latvian beldam named Ilyeana, who welcomed the idea of living in the country with such alacrity I was convinced she must be a fugitive from justice. Her cooking did nothing to contradict the impression; three nights hand running she served mulligan and coffee made in a tin and seemed strangely familiar with the argot of hobo jungles. How near I was to the bull's-eye was revealed a week later with the arrival of a letter sent to Ilyeana by relatives in Canada. She ripped open the envelope and a newspaper clipping fell to the floor. I picked it up and was about to hand it to her when I saw the sinister heading, "Missing Man Believed Found." The Mounties, idly dragging a lake near Moose Jaw, Saskatchewan, had recovered some parcels which, laid end to end, turned out to be the body of a man. "The victim's sister, whom the authorities would like to question," the account added, "is at present thought to be in Latvia." Far from being in Latvia, the victim's sister was standing at that exact moment peering over my shoulder in good old Tinicum Township, Pennsylvania. I cleared my throat and edged a little closer to the fire tongs.

"What do you make of this, Ilyeana?" I asked. I knew damn well what she made of it, but you have to begin somewhere.

"Ah, this happen every time I get good job," she said. "Always pickin' on me. Well, I guess I go up there and take a look at him. I know that head of hair anywhere."

At the station, Ilyeana bought a ticket to Savannah, which would seem a rather circuitous route to the Dominion, but nobody was surpised, least of all the passenger agent. What with people winging through to Martinique, Australia, and similar exotic climes, that little New Jersey depot could give cards and spades to Shepheard's Hotel in Cairo. And speaking of spades, could anybody put me on to one named Uncle Pompey, with a frizzy white poll and a deft hand for grits?

SOMEWHERE A ROSCOE . . .

This is the story of a mind that found itself. About two years ago I was moody, discontented, restless, almost a character in a Russian novel. I used to lie on my bed for days drinking tea out of a glass (I was one of the first in this country to drink tea out of a glass; at that time fashionable people drank from their cupped hands). Underneath, I was still a lively, fun-loving American boy who liked nothing better than to fish with a bent pin. In short, I had become a remarkable combination of Raskolnikov and Mark Tidd.

One day I realized how introspective I had grown and decided to talk to myself like a Dutch uncle. "Luik here, Mynheer," I began (I won't give you the accent, but honestly it was a riot), "you've overtrained. You're stale. Open up a few new vistas—go out and get some fresh air!" Well, I bustled about, threw some things into a bag—orange peels, apple cores and the like—and went out for a walk. A few minutes later I picked up from a park bench a tattered pulp magazine called *Spicy Detective*. . . . Talk about your turning points!

I hope nobody minds my making love in public, but if Culture Publications, Inc., of 900 Market Street, Wilmington, Delaware, will have me, I'd like to marry them. Yes, I know—call it a school-boy crush, puppy love, the senseless infatuation of a callow youth for a middle-aged, worldly-wise publishing house; I still don't care. I love them because they are the publishers of not only *Spicy*

Detective but also *Spicy Western, Spicy Mystery* and *Spicy Adventure*. And I love them most because their prose is so soft and warm.

"Arms and the man I sing," sang Vergil some twenty centuries ago, preparing to celebrate the wanderings of Aeneas. If ever a motto was tailormade for the masthead of Culture Publications, Inc., it is "Arms and the Woman," for in *Spicy Detective* they have achieved the sauciest blend of libido and murder this side of Gilles de Rais. They have juxtaposed the steely automatic and the frilly pantie and found that it pays off. Above all, they have given the world Dan Turner, the apotheosis of all private detectives. Out of Ma Barker by Dashiell Hammett's Sam Spade, let him characterize himself in the opening paragraph of "Corpse in the Closet," from the July, 1937, issue:

> I opened my bedroom closet. A half-dressed feminine corpse sagged into my arms. . . . It's a damned screwy feeling to reach for pajamas and find a cadaver instead.

Mr. Turner, you will perceive, is a man of sentiment, and it occasionally gets him into a tight corner. For example, in "Killer's Harvest" (July, 1938) he is retained to escort a young matron home from the Cocoanut Grove in Los Angeles:

> Zarah Trenwick was a wow in a gown of silver lamé that stuck to her lush curves like a coating of varnish. Her makeup was perfect; her strapless dress displayed plenty of evidence that she still owned a cargo of lure. Her bare shoulders were snowy, dimpled. The upper slopes of her breast were squeezed

upward and partly overflowed the tight bodice, like whipped cream.

To put it mildly, Dan cannot resist the appeal of a pretty foot, and disposing of Zarah's drunken husband ("I clipped him on the button. His hip pockets bounced on the floor"), he takes this charlotte russe to her apartment. Alone with her, the policeman in him succumbs to the man, and "she fed me a kiss that throbbed all the way down my fallen arches," when suddenly:

From the doorway a roscoe said "Kachow!" and a slug creased the side of my noggin. Neon lights exploded inside my think-tank . . . She was as dead as a stuffed mongoose . . . I wasn't badly hurt. But I don't like to be shot at. I don't like dames to be rubbed out when I'm flinging woo at them.

With an irritable shrug, Dan phones the homicide detail and reports Zarah's passing in this tender obituary: "Zarah Trenwick just got blasted to hellangone in her tepee at the Gayboy. Drag your underwear over here— and bring a meat-wagon." Then he goes in search of the offender:

I drove over to Argyle; parked in front of Fane Trenwick's modest stash . . . I thumbed the bell. The door opened. A Chink house-boy gave me the slant-eyed focus. "Missa Tlenwick, him sleep. You go way, come tomollow. Too late fo' vlisito'." I said "Nerts to you, Confucius," and gave him a shove on the beezer.

Zarah's husband, wrenched out of bed without the silly formality of a search warrant, establishes an alibi depending upon one Nadine Wendell. In a trice Dan crosses the city and makes his gentle way into the lady's boudoir, only to discover again what a frail vessel he is au *fond:*

The fragrant scent of her red hair tickled my smeller; the warmth of her slim young form set fire to my arterial system. After all, I'm as human as the next gazabo.

The next gazabo must be all too human, because Dan betrays first Nadine and then her secret; namely, that she pistolled Zarah Trenwick for reasons too numerous to mention. If you feel you must know them, they appear on page 110, cheek by jowl with some fascinating advertisements for loaded dice and wealthy sweethearts, either of which will be sent you in plain wrapper if you'll forward a dollar to the Majestic Novelty Company of Janesville, Wisconsin.

The deeper one goes into the Dan Turner saga, the more one is struck by the similarity between the case confronting Dan in the current issue and those in the past. The murders follow an exact, rigid pattern almost like the ritual of a bullfight or a classic Chinese play. Take "Veiled Lady," in the October, 1937, number of *Spicy Detective.* Dan is flinging some woo at a Mrs. Brantham in her apartment at the exclusive Gayboy Arms, which apparently excludes everybody but assassins:

From behind me a roscoe belched "Chow-chow!" A pair of slugs buzzed past my left ear, almost nicked my cranium. Mrs. Brantham sagged back against the pillow of the lounge . . . She was as dead as an iced catfish.

Or this vignette from "Falling Star," out of the September, 1936, issue.

The roscoe said "Chow!" and spat a streak of flame past my shoulder . . . The Filipino cutie was lying where I'd last seen her. She was as dead as a smoked herring.

And again, from "Dark Star of Death," January, 1938:

From a bedroom a roscoe said: "Whr-r-rang!" and a lead pill split the ozone past my noggin . . . Kane Fewster was on the floor. There was a bullet hole through his think-tank. He was as dead as a fried oyster.

And still again, from "Brunette Bump-off," May, 1938:

And then, from an open window beyond the bed, a roscoe coughed "Ka-chow!" . . . I said, "What the hell—!" and hit the floor with my smeller . . . A brunette jane was lying there, half out of the mussed covers. . . . She was as dead as vaudeville.

The next phase in each of these dramas follows with all the cold beauty and inevitability of a legal brief. The roscoe has hardly spoken, coughed, or belched before Dan is off through the canebrake, his nostrils filled with the heavy scent of Nuit de Noël. Somewhere, in some dimly lit boudoir, waits a voluptuous parcel of womanhood who knows all about the horrid deed. Even if she doesn't, Dan makes a routine check anyway. The premises are invariably guarded by an Oriental whom Dan is obliged to expunge. Compare the scene at Fane Trenwick's modest stash with this one from "Find That Corpse" (November, 1937):

A sleepy Chink maid in pajamas answered my ring. She was a cute little slant-eyed number. I said "Is Mr. Polznak home?" She shook her head. "Him up on location in Flesno. Been gone two week." I said "Thanks. I'll have a gander for myself." I pushed past her. She started to yip . . . "Shut up!" I growled. She kept on trying to make a noise. So I popped her on the button. She dropped.

It is a fairly safe bet that Mr. Polznak has forgotten the adage that a watched pot never boils and has left behind a dewy-eyed coryphée clad in the minimum of chiffon demanded by the postal authorities. The poet in Dan ineluctably vanquishes the flatfoot ("Dark Star of Death"): "I glued my glims on her blond loveliness; couldn't help myself. The covers had skidded down from her gorgeous, dimpled shoulders; I could see plenty of delishful, she-male epidermis." The trumpets blare again; some expert capework by our torero, and "Brunette Bump-off"): "Then she fed me a kiss that sent a charge of steam past my gozzle . . . Well, I'm as human as the next gink."

From then on, the author's typewriter keys infallibly fuse in a lump of hot metal and it's all over but the shouting of the culprit and *Look, Men: One Hundred Breezy Fotos!* Back in his stash, his roscoe safely within reach, Dan Turner lays his weary noggin on a pillow, resting up for the November issue. And unless you're going to need me for something this afternoon, I intend to do the same. I'm *bushed.*

WAITING FOR SANTY

A CHRISTMAS PLAYLET

(With a Bow to Mr. Clifford Odets)

Scene: The sweatshop of S. Claus, a manufacturer of children's toys, on North Pole Street. Time: The night before Christmas.

At rise, seven gnomes, Rankin, Panken, Rivkin, Riskin, Ruskin, Briskin, and Praskin, are discovered working furiously to fill orders piling up at stage right. The whir of lathes, the hum of motors, and the hiss of drying lacquer are so deafening that at times the dialogue cannot be heard, which is very vexing if you vex easily. (Note: The parts of Rankin, Panken, Rivkin, Riskin, Ruskin, Briskin, and Praskin are interchangeable, and may be secured directly from your dealer or the factory.)

RISKIN (filing a Meccano girder, bitterly)—A parasite, a leech, a bloodsucker—altogether a five-star nogoodnick! Starvation wages we get so he can ride around in a red team with reindeers!

RUSKIN (jeering)—Hey, Karl Marx, whyn'tcha hire a hall?

RISKIN (sneering)—Scab! Stool pigeon! Company spy! (They tangle and rain blows on each other. While waiting for these to dry, each returns to his respective task.)

BRISKIN (sadly, to Panken)—All day long I'm painting "Snow Queen" on these Flexible Flyers and my little Irving lays in a cold tenement with the gout.

PANKEN—You said before it was the mumps.

BRISKIN (*with a fatalistic shrug*)—The mumps—the gout—go argue with City Hall.

PANKEN (*kindly, passing him a bowl*)—Here, take a piece fruit.

BRISKIN (*chewing*)—It ain't bad, for wax fruit.

PANKEN (*with pride*)—I painted it myself.

BRISKIN (*rejecting the fruit*)—Ptoo! Slave psychology!

RIVKIN (*suddenly, half to himself, half to the Party*)—I got a belly full of stars, baby. You make me feel like I swallowed a Roman candle.

PRASKIN (*curiously*)—What's wrong with the kid?

RISKIN—What's wrong with all of us? The system! Two years he and Claus's daughter's been making googoo eyes behind the old man's back.

PRASKIN—So what?

RISKIN (*scornfully*)—So what? Economic determinism! What do you think the kid's name is—J. Pierpont Rivkin? He ain't even got for a bottle Dr. Brown's Celery Tonic. I tell you, it's like gall in my mouth two young people shouldn't have a room where they could make great music.

RANKIN (*warningly*)—Shhh! Here she comes now! (*Stella Claus enters, carrying a portable phonograph. She and Rivkin embrace, place a record on the turntable, and begin a very slow waltz, unmindful that the phonograph is playing "Cohen on the Telephone."*)

STELLA (*dreamily*)—Love me, sugar?

RIVKIN—I can't sleep, I can't eat, that's how I love you. You're a double malted with two scoops of whipped cream; you're the moon rising over Mosholu Parkway;

16

you're a two weeks' vacation at Camp Nitgedaiget! I'd pull down the Chrysler Building to make a bobbie pin for your hair!

STELLA—I've got a stomach full of anguish. Oh, Rivvy, what'll we do?"

PANKEN (*sympathetically*)—Here, try a piece fruit.

RIVKIN (*fiercely*)—Wax fruit—that's been my whole life! Imitations! Substitutes! Well, I'm through! Stella, tonight I'm telling your old man. He can't play mumblety-peg with two human beings! (*The tinkle of sleigh bells is heard offstage, followed by a voice shouting, "Whoa, Dasher! Whoa, Dancer!" A moment later S. Claus enters in a gust of mock snow. He is a pompous bourgeois of sixty-five who affects a white beard and a false air of benevolence. But tonight the ruddy color is missing from his cheeks, his step falters, and he moves heavily. The gnomes hastily replace the marzipan they have been filching.*)

STELLA (*anxiously*)—Papa! What did the specialist say to you?

CLAUS (*brokenly*)—The biggest professor in the country . . . the best cardiac man that money could buy. . . . I tell you I was like a wild man.

STELLA—Pull yourself together, Sam!

CLAUS—It's no use. Adhesions, diabetes, sleeping sickness, decalcomania—oh, my God! I got to cut out climbing in chimneys, he says—me, Sanford Claus, the biggest toy concern in the world!

STELLA (*soothingly*)—After all, it's only one man's opinion.

CLAUS—No, no, he cooked my goose. I'm like a broken uke after a Yosian picnic. Rivkin!

RIVKIN—Yes, Sam.

CLAUS—My boy, I had my eye on you for a long time. You and Stella thought you were too foxy for an old man, didn't you? Well, let bygones be bygones. Stella, do you love this gnome?

STELLA (*simply*)—He's the whole stage show at the Music Hall, Papa; he's Toscanini conducting Beethoven's Fifth; he's—

CLAUS (*curtly*)—Enough already. Take him. From now on he's a partner in the firm. (*As all exclaim, Claus holds up his hand for silence.*) And tonight he can take my route and make the deliveries. It's the least I could do for my own flesh and blood. (*As the happy couple kiss, Claus wipes away a suspicious moisture and turns to the other gnomes.*) Boys, do you know what day tomorrow is?

GNOMES (*crowding around expectantly*)—Christmas!

CLAUS—Correct. When you look in your envelopes tonight, you'll find a little present from me—a forty-percent pay cut. And the first one who opens his trap—gets this. (*As he holds up a tear-gas bomb and beams at them, the gnomes utter cries of joy, join hands, and dance around him shouting exultantly. All except Riskin and Briskin, that is, who exchange a quick glance and go underground.*)

CURTAIN

THE IDOL'S EYE

I had been week-ending with Gabriel Snubbers at his villa, "The Acacias," on the edge of the Downs. Gabriel isn't seen about as much as he used to be; one hears that an eccentric aunt left him a tidy little sum and the lazy beggar refuses to leave his native haunts. Four of us had cycled down from London together: Gossip Gabrilowitsch, the Polish pianist; Downey Couch, the Irish tenor; Frank Falcovsky, the Jewish prowler, and myself, Clay Modelling. Snubbers, his face beaming, met us at the keeper's lodge. His eyes were set in deep rolls of fat for our arrival, and I couldn't help thinking how well they looked. I wondered whether it was because his daring farce, *Mrs. Stebbins' Step-Ins*, had been doing so well at the Haymarket.

"Deuced decent of you chaps to make this filthy trip," he told us, leading us up the great avenue of two stately alms toward the house. "Rum place, this." A surprise awaited us when we reached the house, for the entire left wing had just burned down. Snubbers, poor fellow, stared at it a bit ruefully, I thought.

"Just as well. It was only a plague-spot," sympathized Falcovsky. Snubbers was thoughtful.

"D'ye know, you chaps," he said suddenly, "I could swear an aunt of mine was staying in that wing." Falcovsky stirred the ashes with his stick and uncovered a pair of knitting needles and a half-charred corset.

"No, it must have been the other wing," dismissed

19

Snubbers. "How about a spot of whisky and soda?" We entered and Littlejohn, Snubbers' man, brought in a spot of whisky on a piece of paper which we all examined with interest. A splendid fire was already roaring in the middle of the floor to drive out the warmth.

"Soda?" offered Snubbers. I took it to please him, for Gabriel's cellar was reputedly excellent. A second later I wished that I had drunk the cellar instead. Baking soda is hardly the thing after a three-hour bicycle trip.

"You drank that like a little soldier," he complimented, his little button eyes fastened on me. I was about to remark that I had never drunk a little soldier, when I noticed Littlejohn hovering in the doorway.

"Yes, that will be all," Snubbers waved, "and, oh, by the way, send up to London tomorrow for a new wing, will you?" Littlejohn bowed and left, silently, sleekly Oriental.

"Queer cove, Littlejohn," commented Snubbers. "Shall I tell you a story?" He did, and it was one of the dullest I have ever heard. At the end of it Falcovsky grunted. Snubbers surveyed him suspiciously.

"Why, what's up, old man?" he queried.

"What's up? Nothing's up," snarled Falcovsky. "Can't a man grunt in front of an open fire if he wants to?"

"But . . ." began Snubbers.

"But nothing," Falcovsky grated. "You haven't lived till you've grunted in front of an open fire. Just for that— grunt, grunt, grunt," and he grunted several times out of sheer spite. The baking soda was beginning to tell on Snubbers.

"Remarkable thing happened the other day," he began. "I was pottering about in the garden . . ."

"Why must one always potter around in a garden?" demanded Couch. "Can't you potter around in an arm-chair just as well?"

"I did once," confessed Snubbers moodily, revealing a whitish scar on his chin. "Gad, sir, what a wildcat she was!" He chewed his wad of carbon paper reminiscently. "Oh, well, never mind. But as I was saying—I was going through some of my great-grandfather's things the other day . . ."

"What things?" demanded Falcovsky.

"His bones, if you must know," Snubbers said coldly. "You know, Great-grandfather died under strange cir-cumstances. He opened a vein in his bath."

"I never knew baths had veins," protested Gabril-owitsch.

"I never knew his great-grandfather had a ba—" began Falcovsky derisively. With a shout Snubbers threw him-self on Falcovsky. It was the signal for Pandemonium, the upstairs girl, to enter and throw herself with a shout on Couch. The outcome of the necking bee was as follows: Canadians 12, Visitors 9. Krebs and Vronsky played footie, subbing for Gerber and Weinwald, who were disabled by flying antipasto.

We were silent after Snubbers had spoken; men who have wandered in far places have an innate delicacy about their great-grandfathers' bones. Snubbers' face was a mask, his voice a harsh whip of pain in the stillness when he spoke again.

"I fancy none of you knew my great-grandfather," he said slowly. "Before your time, I daresay. A rare giant of a man with quizzical eyes and a great shock of wiry red hair, he had come through the Peninsular Wars without a scratch. Women loved this impetual Irish adventurer who would rather fight than eat and vice versa. The wars over, he turned toward cookery, planning to devote his failing years to the perfection of the welsh rarebit, a dish he loved. One night he was chafing at The Bit, a tavern in Portsmouth, when he overheard a chance remark from a brawny gunner's mate in his cups. In Calcutta the man had heard native tales of a mysterious idol, whose single eye was a flawless ruby.

" 'Topscuttle my bamberger, it's the size of a bloomin' pigeon's egg!' spat the salt, shifting his quid to his other cheek. 'A bloomin' rajah's ransom and ye may lay to that, mateys!'

"The following morning the *Maid of Hull*, a frigate of the line mounting thirty-six guns, out of Bath and into bed in a twinkling, dropped downstream on the tide, bound out for Bombay, object matrimony. On her as passenger went my great-grandfather, an extra pair of nankeen pants and a dirk his only baggage. Fifty-three days later in Poona, he was heading for the interior of one of the Northern states. Living almost entirely on cameo brooches and the few ptarmigan which fell to the ptrigger of his pfowlingpiece, he at last sighted the towers of Ishpeming, the Holy City of the Surds and Cosines, fanatic Mohammedan warrior sects. He disguised himself as a beggar and entered the gates.

"For weeks my great-grandfather awaited his chance to enter the temple of the idol. They were changing the guard one evening when he saw it. One of the native janissaries dropped his knife. My great-grandfather leaped forward with cringing servility and returned it to him, in the small of his back. Donning the soldier's turban, he quickly slipped into his place. Midnight found him within ten feet of his prize. Now came the final test. He furtively drew from the folds of his robes a plate of curry, a dish much prized by Indians, and set it in a far corner. The guards rushed upon it with bulging squeals of delight. A twist of his wrist and the gem was his. With an elaborately stifled yawn, my great-grandfather left under pretense of going out for a glass of water. The soldiers winked slyly but when he did not return after two hours, their suspicions were aroused. They hastily made a canvass of the places where water was served and their worst fears were realized. The ruby in his burnoose, Great-grandfather was escaping by fast elephant over the Khyber Pass. Dockside loungers in Yarmouth forty days later stared curiously at a mammoth of a man with flaming red hair striding toward the Bull and Bloater Tavern. Under his belt, did they but only know it, lay the Ruby Eye.

"Ten years to that night had passed, and my great-grandfather, in seclusion under this very roof, had almost forgotten his daring escapade. Smoking by the fireplace, he listened to the roar of the wind and reviewed his campaigns. Suddenly he leaped to his feet—a dark face had vanished from the window. Too late my great-grand-father snatched up powder and ball and sent a charge hurtling into the night. The note pinned to the window drained the blood from his face.

"It was the first of a series. Overnight his hair turned from rose-red to snow-white. And finally, when it seemed as though madness were to rob them of their revenge, *they came*."

Snubbers stopped, his eyes those of a man who had looked beyond life and had seen things best left hidden from mortal orbs. Falcovsky's hand was trembling as he pressed a pinch of snuff against his gums.

"You—you mean?" he quavelled.

"Yes." Snubbers' voice had sunk to a whisper. "He fought with the strength of nine devils, but the movers took away his piano. You see," he added very gently, "Great-grandfather had missed the last four instalments." Gabrilowitsch sighed deeply and arose, his eyes fixed intently on Snubbers.

"And—and the ruby?" he asked softly, his delicate fingers closing around the fire-tongs.

"Oh, *that*," shrugged Snubbers, "I just threw that in to make it interesting."

We bashed in his conk and left him to the vultures.

BEAUTY
AND THE BEE

It is always something of a shock to approach a newsstand which handles trade publications and find the *Corset and Underwear Review* displayed next to the *American Bee Journal*. However, newsstands make strange bedfellows, as anyone who has ever slept with a newsstand can testify, and if you think about it at all (instead of sitting there in a torpor with your mouth half-open) you'd see this proximity is not only alphabetical. Both the *Corset and Underwear Review* and the *American Bee Journal* are concerned with honeys; although I am beast enough to prefer a photograph of a succulent nymph in satin Lastex Girdleiere with Thrill Plus Bra to the most dramatic snapshot of an apiary, each has its place in my scheme.

The *Corset and Underwear Review*, which originates at the Haire Publishing Company, 1170 Broadway, New York City, is a magazine for jobbers. Whatever else a corset jobber is, he is certainly nobody's fool. The first seventy pages of the magazine comprise an album of superbly formed models posed in various attitudes of sweet surrender and sheathed in cunning artifices of whalebone, steel, and webbing. Some indication of what Milady uses to give herself a piquant front elevation may be had from the following list of goodies displayed at the Hotel McAlpin Corset Show, reported by the March, 1935, *Corset and Underwear Review*: "Flashes and Filmys, Speedies and Flexees, Sensations and Thrills, Snugfits and Even-Puls, Rite-Flex and Free-Flex, Smooth·

ies and Silk-Skins, Imps and Teens, La Triques and Waikikis, Sis and Modern Miss, Sta-Downs and Props, Over-Tures and Reflections, Lilys and Irenes, Willo-th-wisps and Willoways, Miss Smartie and MisSimplicity, Princess Youth and Princess Chic, Miss Today and Soiree, Kordettes and Francettes, Paristyles and Rengo Belts, Vassarettes and Foundettes, Fans and Fade Aways, Beau Sveltes and Beau Formas, Madame Adrienne and Miss Typist, Stout-eze and Laceze, Symphony and Rhapsody, Naturade and Her Secret, Rollees and Twin Tops, Charma and V-Ette, La Camille and La Tec."

My neck, ordinarily an alabaster column, began to turn a dull red as I forged through the pages of the *Corset and Underwear Review* into the section called "Buyer News." Who but Sir John Suckling could have achieved the leering sensuality of a poem by Mrs. Adelle Mahone, San Francisco representative of the Hollywood-Maxwell Company, whom the magazine dubs "The Brassière Bard of the Bay District"?

> Out-of-town buyers!—during your stay
> At the McAlpin, see our new display.
> There are bras for the young, support for the old,
> Up here for the shy, down to there for the bold.
> We'll have lace and nets and fabrics such as
> Sturdy broadcloths and satins luscious.
> We'll gladly help your profits transform
> If you'll come up to our room and watch us perform.
> Our new numbers are right from the Coast:
> Snappy and smart, wait!—we must not boast—
> We'll just urge you to come and solicit your smiles,
> So drop in and order your Hollywood styles.

One leaves the lacy *chinoiseries* of the *Corset and Underwear Review* with reluctance and turns to the bucolic *American Bee Journal*, published at Hamilton, Illinois, by C. P. Dadant. Here Sex is whittled down to a mere nubbin; everything is as clean as a whistle and as dull as a hoe. The bee is the *petit bourgeois* of the insect world, and his keeper is a self-sufficient stooge who needs and will get no introduction to you. The pages of the *American Bee Journal* are studded with cocky little essays like "Need of Better Methods of Controlling American Foulbrood" and "The Swarming Season in Manitoba." It is only in "The Editor's Answers, a query column conducted by Mr. Dadant, that Mr. Average Beekeeper removes his mask and permits us to peep at the warm, vibrant human beneath. The plight of the reader who signs himself "Illinois" (I've seen *that* name somewhere) is typical:

I would like to know the easiest way to get a swarm of bees which are lodged in between the walls of a house. The walls are of brick and they are in the dead-air space. They have been there for about three years. I would like to know method to use to get the bees, not concerned about the honey.

The editor dismisses the question with some claptrap about a "bee smoker" which is too ridiculous to repeat. The best bet I see for "Illinois" is to play upon the weakness of all bees. Take a small boy smeared with honey and lower him between the walls. The bees will fasten themselves to him by the hundreds and can be scraped off when he is pulled up, after which the boy can be thrown away. If no small boy smeared with honey can be found, it may be necessary to take an ordinary small boy and smear him, which should be a pleasure.

From the Blue Grass comes an even more perplexed letter:

I have been ordering a few queens every year and they are always sent as first-class mail and are thrown off the fast trains that pass here at a speed of 60 miles an hour. Do you think it does the queens any harm by throwing them off these fast trains? You know they get an awful jolt when they hit the ground. Some of these queens are very slow about doing anything after they are put in the hive.—KENTUCKY.

I have no desire to poach on George Washington Cable's domain, but if that isn't the furthest North in Southern gallantry known to man, I'll eat his collected works in Macy's window at high noon. It will interest every lover of chivalry to know that since the above letter was published, queen bees in the Blue Grass have been treated with new consideration by railroad officials. A Turkey-red carpet similar to that used by the Twentieth Century Limited is now unrolled as the train stops, and each queen, blushing to the very roots of her antennae, is escorted to her hive by a uniformed porter. The rousing strains of the cakewalk, the comical antics of the darkies, the hiss of fried chicken sputtering in the pan, all combine to make the scene unforgettable.

But the predicament of both "Illinois" and "Kentucky" pale into insignificance beside the problem presented by another reader:

I have been asked to "talk on bees" at a nearby church some evening in the fall. Though I have kept bees for ten years, I am "scared stiff" because not a man in the audience knows a thing about bees and I am afraid of being too technical.

I plan to take along specimens of queen, drone and worker, also a glass observatory hive with bees, smoker and tools, an extra hive, and possibly some queen cell cups, etc.

Could you suggest any manipulating that might be done for the "edification of the audience"? I've seen pictures of stunts that have been worked, like making a beard of bees; and I've heard of throwing the bees out in a ball only to have them return to the hive without bothering anyone. But, I don't know how these stunts are done, nor do I know of any that I could do with safety. (I don't mind getting a sting or two myself, but I don't want anyone in the audience to get stung, or I might lose my audience.)

I've only opened hives a few times at night, but never liked the job as the bees seem to fly up into the light and sting very readily. That makes me wonder whether any manipulating can be done in a room at night.

How long before the affair would I need to have the bees in the room to have them settle down to the hive?—New York.

The only thing wrong with "New York" is that he just doesn't like bees. In one of those unbuttoned moods everybody has, a little giddy with cocoa and crullers, he allowed himself to be cajoled by the vestrymen, and now, face to face with his ordeal, he is sick with loathing for bees and vestrymen alike. There is one solution, however, and that is for "New York" to wrap himself tightly in muslin the night of the lecture and stay in bed with his hat on. If the vestrymen come for him, let him throw the bees out in a ball. To hell with whether they return or not, and that goes for the vestrymen, too. It certainly goes for me. If I ever see the postman trudging toward my house with a copy of the *American Bee Journal*, I'm going to lodge myself in the dead-air space between the walls and no amount of small boys smeared with honey will ever get me out. And you be careful, *American Bee Journal—I bite.*

IS THERE AN OSTEO-SYNCHRONDROITRICIAN IN THE HOUSE?

Looking back at it now, I see that every afternoon at 4:30 for the past five months I had fallen into an exact routine. First off, I'd tap the dottle from my pipe by knocking it against the hob. I never smoke a pipe, but I like to keep one with a little dottle in it, and an inexpensive hob to tap it against; when you're in the writing game, there are these little accessories you need. Then I'd slip off my worn old green smoking jacket, which I loathe, and start down Lexington Avenue for home. Sometimes, finding myself in my shirtsleeves, I would have to return to my atelier for my jacket and overcoat, but as I say, when you're in the writing game, its strictly head-in-the-clouds. Now, Lexington Avenue is Lexington Avenue—when you've once seen Bloomingdale's and the Wil-Low Cafeteria, you don't go nostalgic all over as you might for the Avenue de l'Observatoire and the Closerie des Lilas.

Anyway, I'd be head down and scudding along under bare poles by the time I reached the block between Fifty-eighth and Fifty-seventh Streets, and my glance into those three shop windows would be purely automatic. First, the highly varnished *Schnecken* in the bakery; then the bones of a human foot shimmying slowly on a near-mahogany pedestal in the shoestore; and finally the clock set in the heel of a congress gaiter at the bootblack's. By now my shabby old reflexes would tell me it was time to buy an evening paper and bury my head in it. A little whim of my wife's; she liked to dig it up, as a puppy does a bone, while I was sipping my cocktail. Later on I taught her to frisk with a ball of yarn, but to get back to what happened Washington's Birthday.

I was hurrying homeward that holiday afternoon pretty much in the groove, humming an aria from "Till Tom Special" and wishing I could play the clarinet like a man named Goodman. Just as it occurred to me that I might drug this individual and torture his secret out of him, I came abreast the window of the shoestore containing the bones of the human foot. My mouth suddenly developed that curious dry feeling when I saw that they were vibrating, as usual, from north to south, every little metatarsal working with the blandest contempt for all I hold dear. I pressed my ear against the window and heard the faint clicking of the motor housed in the box beneath. A little scratch here and there on the shellac surface showed where one of the more enterprising toes had tried to do a solo but had quickly rejoined the band. Not only was the entire arch rolling forward and backward in an oily fashion, but it had evolved an obscene side sway at the same time, a good deal like the *danse à ventre*. Maybe the foot had belonged to an Ouled-Naïl girl, but I felt I didn't care to find out. I was aware immediately of an active desire to rush home and lie down attended by my loved ones. The only trouble was that when I started to leave the place, I could feel my arches acting according to all the proper orthopedic laws, and I swear people turned to look at me as if they heard a clicking sound.

The full deviltry of the thing only became apparent as I lay on my couch a bit later, a vinegar poultice on my forehead, drinking a cup of steaming tea. That little bevy of bones had been oscillating back and forth all through Danzig, Pearl Harbor, and the North African campaign; this very minute it was undulating turgidly, heedless of the fact the store had been closed two hours. Furthermore, if its progress were not impeded by the two wires snaffled to the toes (I'll give you *that* thought to thrash around with some sleepless night), it might by now have encircled the world five times, with a stopover at the Eucharistic Congress. For a moment the implications were so shocking that I started up alarmed. But since my loved ones had gone off to the movies and there was nobody to impress, I turned over and slept like a top, with no assistance except three and a half grains of barbital.

I could have reached my workshop the next morning by walking up Third Avenue, taking a cab up Lexington, or even crawling on my hands and knees past the shoe-store to avoid that indecent window display, but my feet won their unequal struggle with my brain and carried me straight to the spot. Staring hypnotized at the macabre shuffle (halfway between a rhumba and a soft-shoe step), I realized that I was receiving a sign from above to take the matter in hand. I spent the morning shopping lower Third Avenue, and at noon, dressed as an attaché of the Department of Sanitation, began to lounge nonchalantly before the store. My broom was getting nearer and nearer the window when the manager came out noiselessly. My ducks must have been too snowy, for he gave one of his clerks a signal and a moment later a policeman turned the corner. Fortunately, I had hidden my civvies in the lobby of Proctor's Fifty-eighth Street Theatre, and by the time the breathless policeman rushed in, I had approached the wicket as cool as a cucumber, asked for two cucumbers in the balcony, and signed my name for Bank Nite. I flatter myself that I brought off the affair rather well.

My second attempt, however, was as fruitless as the first. I padded my stomach with a pillow, grayed my hair at the temples, and entered the shop fiercely. Pointing to the white piping on my vest, I represented myself as a portly banker from Portland, Maine, and asked the manager what he would take for the assets and good will, spot cash. I was about to make him a firm offer when I found myself being escorted out across the sidewalk, the manager's foot serving as fulcrum.

And there, precisely, the matter rests. I have given plenty of thought to the problem, and there is only one solution. Are there three young men in this city, with stout hearts and no dependents, who know what I mean? We can clean out that window with two well-directed grenades and get away over the rooftops. Given half a break, we'll stop that grisly *pas seul* ten seconds after we pull out the pins with our teeth. If we're caught, there's always the cyanide in our belts. First meeting tonight at nine in front of the Railroad Men's Y.M.C.A., and wear a blue cornflower. *Up the rebels!*

ABBY, THIS IS YOUR FATHER

A certain five-cent weekly published in Philadelphia with a sworn circulation of 3,100,000 has been given lately to a good deal of blushing and stammering and other signs of pretty confusion. Naturally I cannot violate professional ethics by using real names, but, spelled backward, the legend on the magazine runs "Tsop Gnineve Yadrutas Eht" (a catchy enough title for any reader's money), and it was founded Anno Domini 1728 by Beljamir Flankler. I fope I mek misef clirr.

The reason for all this dimpling and coloring up to the roots of the hair is something the editors are modest enough to term "Post Luck." On a number of occasions their articles have been so timely as to seem almost clairvoyant. For example, a biography of Will Rogers had barely concluded before his death was announced, and similarly General Walter Krivitsky, *geboren* Schmelka Ginzberg, forecast the Russo-German nuptials at a time when the happy couple was still issuing denials to friends and relatives. Whatever the mysterious pipeline it possesses to the infinite, the *Post* is constantly hiring the back page of the New York *Times* to kiss its reflection in the mirror and murmur, "Oo, you pitty sing." Throughout which, of course, *Collier's* waspishly pats its back hair into place and pretends to be looking the other way. But not long ago, baker-fresh from the editorial oven and as if to confound the skeptics, there came another startling proof of the *Post's* telepathy. The place of honor in one of the late autumn issues was given over to the opening install-ment of *Mary, This Is Your Mother*, by Catherine Hayes Brown, subheaded "The Unique Story of Helen Hayes, as Told by Her Mother." Now hold your hats. Less than a month before that, *Ladies and Gentlemen*, a new play by Charles MacArthur and Ben Hecht, opened in New York, and in its leading rôle was *Helen Hayes!* Why, it's enough to make a body's flesh creep.

The epistolary form is a mold sanctified in the editorial rooms of the *Post*, where it is still remembered that George Horace Lorimer, the Great White Father of the Curtis publications, made a sizable bale of scratch out of a little book called *Letters of a Self-Made Merchant to His Son*. How many editions this early classic attained I do not know, but the last time I wandered down Fourth Avenue it still covered the second-hand bookstores like a mulch. The tradition was subsequently carried forward in the pages of the *Post* by William Hazlett Upson with his letters of a tractor salesman, and now, as the torch drops from his nerveless hand, Mrs. Brown picks it up with *Mary, This Is Your Mother*. To me, it seems a rather roundabout way of telling a child about its mother to write it letters in a magazine which costs a nickel, when you can deal out a few crisp facts right in the kitchen, but I suppose it cuts down the back talk considerably.

As if this whole affair were not spooky enough already, the very week Mrs. Brown began her revelations the pres-ent writer's mother was on the verge of publishing some letters dealing with his career which she had written to her granddaughter. They reveal an astonishing parallel to

Mrs. Brown's letters and one that should prove interesting to all lovers of good clean parallels. In reading them, it is well to remember that many portions are in anapaestic pentameter, as they were intended to be sung through tissue paper stretched over a comb. No attempt has been made to edit the letters other than removing the checks they contained and cashing them.

ABBY DEAR:

I am going to write you a lot of letters about your daddy's early life, and you just try and stop me. And that goes for him too. And what's more, I'm going to get them printed if I have to do it on a hand press. A Mr. Caxton in the next block, who is very clever about such things, has just invented movable type, and he has promised to help me.

Enclosed is a little remembrance for your birthday. The green stones are what we call emeralds, the white sparkly ones diamonds. It costs about $585,000; it is not much to look at, but will do you for rainy days.

Lovingly,
GRANDMA

ABBY DEAR:

I suppose you often wonder what your daddy was like as a small boy. Well, he was just the most serious and sober little man you can imagine. He had a long, drooping Velvet Joe mustache, dipped snuff constantly, and was head bookkeeper for Portfolio & Dugdale, the corn factors. I don't think he ever really cared much about his wife, though he adored his children (he had three by the time he was seven years old). He was always moping around in a brown study, and when people spoke to him he would listen with only half an ear. To do him justice, that was all he had; the balance had been cropped for thievery, so you can see he had something to mope about.

When he was about eight, he stopped talking altogether, and I took him to Italy in an effort to revive his spirits. He spoke only once. We were floating along the Grand Canal in a gondola when a man attired as a Venetian nobleman of the fourteenth century lost his footing and toppled off the Bridge of Sighs. Your daddy smiled wanly and remarked to nobody in particular, "It shouldn't happen to a doge."

I know how fond you are of driving around these brisk autumn days, but you must see your pony doesn't catch cold. Wouldn't we feel awful if Toby dropped dead of pneumonia or something? I have had Jaeckel's stitch several chinchilla coats into a warm rug for him, and make sure he takes it off when he comes into the house.

Devotedly,

GRANDMA

ABBY DEAR:

By the time your daddy was eleven, he had made enough money to retire and give up all his time to translating the works of Elbert Hubbard, the Sage of Aurora, into Armenian, which he claimed would out-sell *The Trail of the Lonesome Pine*. Unfortunately, like all successful men, he had made a good many enemies in business, and when the book came out they went around talking against it, so it didn't do as well as some other books that year. Then his enemies started pounding him on Wall Street and brought on the panic of 1907, and your daddy lost every penny. It is to his credit that he sat down without a whimper and wrote Bleak House, The Gilded Age, and a host of other successful novels which paid off every last creditor. But he was thirteen when he finished, and a man broken in health.

During your father's convalescence at Savin Rock, your Uncle Hosea—you remember, he was a famous oarsman at New Haven—came to visit us. As he alighted from the train, the Yale crew was having its annual banquet there and they recognized him. A cheer went up, and one of their number swung Uncle Hosea over his shoulder and bore him, kicking and screaming, through the streets. I was naturally alarmed at Hosea's tardiness in arriving, and expressed my anxiety. "We tried to keep it from you," remarked your daddy, "but poor Uncle Hosea was carried off by a stroke."

Under separate cover I am sending you an amusing keepsake, a string of pearls that once belonged to Maria Theresa of Austria. They are not in very good condition; however, you can knot the four strands together and use them for skipping rope.

Always,
Grandma

Abby Dear:

I know that the question uppermost in your mind is where your daddy spent the years between fifteen and twenty-one. The explanation he gives to the world is that although Moriarty lay at the bottom of the Reichenbach Fall, there still remained at large the *second* most dangerous man in London, Colonel Sebastian Moran. Until such time as Moran would show his hand, your daddy says he amused himself by traveling in Tibet, paying a short but interesting visit to the Khalifa at Khartoum (the results of which he communicated to the Foreign Office), and doing some research into the coal-tar derivatives at Montpellier. I may say that the whole story is a pack of lies.

The real facts are these. On his fifteenth birthday I took your daddy to a matinée at the Apollo Burlesk and afterward to Schrafft's, where he had three mint smashes. On our way home we stopped in front of one of those shoddy auction rooms which line West Forty-second Street. The auctioneer exhibited a hideous brown jardinière and offered it to the first bidder. Next to us in the crowd stood a lady holding by the hand her child, who chanced to be a Siamese twin. Each of the twins wore on his head one of those aviator helmets so popular with children. "Just a moment," interposed your daddy loudly, "the pot goes to this lady here!" "Why?" scowled the auctioneer. "Because she's got a pair of aces back to back," returned your daddy. The crowd immediately rushed him and inflicted such damage that we were six years restoring his face to a condition where dogs no longer howled when they saw him.

Do you know where the Tebo Yacht Basin is, dear? Well, the next time you are in New York and find your hotel tiresome, tell the cab driver to take you over to Brooklyn and go aboard the *Corsair II*. I bought it for you from Mr. Morgan and it might be a lark to spend the night on your very own little boat. When you leave, don't forget to tell the captain to scuttle it, and oblige

Your ever-adoring

GRANDMA

BUFFALOS OF THE WORLD, UNITE!

Anybody who happened to be a buffalo last year (or was supporting during his taxable year one or more buffalos closely dependent upon him) is going to have a pretty hollow feeling in the pit of his stomach when he gets a hinge at the July issue of *The Field*. In that excellent British sporting magazine, one "Old Harrow Boy" attacks the custom of shouting and waving the arms and hat to break up stampeding buffalos, and actually suggests *whistling* as a better means of dispersing unlawful assemblages of bison.

I hold no buff for the briefalo—I beg pardon, I should have said "I hold no brief for the buffalo," but I am too choked with rage about this matter to be very coherent. I have never taken money from any pro-bison organization and outside of a fatty deposit between the shoulder blades I am no more buffalo than you are. But of all the appalling, repellent, revolting and insupportable bits of *Schrecklichkeit* ever fobbed off on a lethargic public under the guise of sportsmanship, this is the absolute pay-off.

First, just who *is* this "Old Harrow Boy" anyway? I looked him up in the London Street directory but the only name like it was "O'Hara Roy, 15, Pig's Walk, Wapping Old Stairs." "Pig's Walk" is good; "Pig's Talk," if you ask me. A man who hasn't even got the nerve to sign his own name to a letter. Well, Mr. O'Hara, let's cast an eye over your record and see who it is that goes around lousing up a buffalo's good name. It might interest you to know that I sent a friend of mine around to Wapping Old Stairs to ask a few questions. I believe he came to your service flat one afternoon and talked to your "housekeeper." But you thought he was some kind of an idiot, eh? Well, he is. He's one of the most all-around idiots I know, but there's one thing about him. He doesn't spend his day teasing buffalos. He leaves that to a certain pig in Wapping Old Stairs. No need to mention names.

Among other things I was interested to learn that our precious Mr. O'Hara had been tried and convicted in Rhodesia for acting as *agent-provocateur* in an uprising of water buffalos in 1911. Shortly afterward three buffalos reported to the British High Commissioner at Elandfontein that they had been bored by Mr. O'Hara. The seriousness of the charge forced the Commissioner's hand, and an investigation was held. It revealed that O'Hara had approached the buffalos in a kind of hysterical, excited fashion and told them some rambling inconsequential story without any point. The bisons alleged boredom and petitioned for damages. I have been in correspondence with Sir Herbert Antinous (then Sir Herbert Antinous) who acted as medical officer in the case. He has been kind enough to forward me a transcript of the evidence together with a locket containing hair from one of the buffalos as proof. Here is Sir Herbert's version of the matter:

"I examined the three buffalos about an hour after they claimed Mr. O'Hara had bored them. They still bore the marks of their recent ordeal. One of them had a coated tongue and was feverish. The second seemed normal but slightly bemused. The third, however, had no tongue. I guess the cat got it. (*Laughter.*)

"*Question from Magistrate Nirdlinger:* Sir Herbert, kindly confine yourself to the case. What is the difference between a Florida orange and a letter?

"*Sir Herbert:* I don't know, Your Worship."

"*Nirdlinger:* Well, you'd be a hell of a man to send to mail a letter. Stand down."

At this point there was a commotion in court caused by O'Hara's pitching forward out of the dock in a dead faint. The session was adjourned to allow Sir Herbert to examine the prisoner. Here is his version of the case:

"I examined O'Hara about five minutes after he pitched forward out of the dock in a dead faint. He still bore the marks of his recent ordeal. He had a coated tongue and was feverish."

The subsequent history of the case is completely without interest. The accused's counsel entered a plea of *prosit* and O'Hara was lashed to the mizzen and given five dozen with the cat, who seemed to be in good condition except for a slightly coated tongue.

This, then, is the man who advocates whistling at stampeding buffalos. This unctuous traitor, writing on foolscap in onion juice, who signs fictitious names to his slanders, dares undermine an institution as hallowed as waving one's hat at buffalos. Ever since the days of Buffon, the naturalist, it has gone without saying that the first thing you do on seeing a buffalo is shout and wave your arms and hat. But no; that's not good enough for O'Hara. *He* has to put on side. *He* has to make a holy show out of himself in front of animals, let alone the Kaffir boys. And maybe you don't think the Kaffir boys talk! Only last night old man Kaffir and his youngest boy Morris came into a poolroom in Spion Kop. Morris had two beers and started talking. Well, sir, he talked pretty near two hours before they could stop him. I just mention this to show how the Kaffir boys talk once they get started.

Well, O'Hara, I've said my say. I'm a plain-spoken, grizzled old seadog, none of your French airs for old Peleg Starbuck. Why, bless your heart, boy, I was a powder monkey aboard the old *Guerriere* afore you was born. I've been a galley slave aboard the pirate proas of the Dey of Algiers, I've been shipwrecked among the head-hunting Dyaks, pursued by Arab dhows in the Straits of Aden, and careened in the Dry Tortugas. But don't you heed this old man's talk; you young folks go along and have a look through my spyglass. What's that you say—a suspicious moisture in my eye? Pshaw—a bit of rain, shiver my blini. And coughing to hide his embarrassment, old Peleg hobbled up the shell-decorated path to his cottage as Frederica and I spat reflectively on his peonies and turned our faces toward Ostable and the setting sun.

SAUCE FOR THE GANDER

Every so often, when business slackens up in the bowling alley and the other pin boys are hunched over their game of bezique, I like to exchange my sweatshirt for a crisp white surgical tunic, polish up my optical mirror, and examine the corset advertisements in the New York *Herald Tribune* rotogravure section and the various women's magazines. It must be made clear at the outset that my motives are the purest and my curiosity that of the scientific research worker rather than the sex maniac. Of course, I can be broken down under cross-examination; I like a trim ankle as well as anyone, but once I start scrubbing up and adjusting the operative mask, Materia Medica comes in the door and Betty Grable flics out the window.

God knows how the convention ever got started, but if it is true that the camera never lies, a foundation garment or a girdle stimulates the fair sex to a point just this side of madness. The little ladies are always represented with their heads thrown back in an attitude of fierce desire, arms upflung to an unseen deity as though swept along in some Dionysian revel. If you hold your ear close enough to the printed page, you can almost hear the throbbing of the temple drums and the chant of the votaries. Those sultry, heavy-lidded glances, those tempestuous, Corybantic gestures of abandon—what magic property is there in an ordinary silk-and-Lastex bellyband to cause a housewife to behave like Little Egypt?

Perhaps the most curious mutation of the corset advertisement is the transformation, or clinical type, consisting of two photographs. The first shows a rather bedraggled young matron in a gaping, misshapen girdle at least half a dozen sizes too large for her, cringing under the cool inspection of a trained nurse and several friends. Judging from the flowers and the tea service, the hostess has invited her neighbors in to deride her physique, for they are exclaiming in unison, "Ugh, my dear—you've got *lordosis* [unlovely bulge and sagging backline]!" The second photograph, naturally, depicts the miracles wrought by the proper girdle, which, in addition to the benefits promised in the text, seems to have removed the crow's feet from under the subject's eyes, marcelled her hair, reupholstered the divan, and papered the walls.

It strikes me that, by contrast, the manufacturers of dainty underthings for men have been notably colorless in their advertising. The best they are able to afford are those static scenes in which four or five grim-jawed industrialists stand about a locker room in their shorts scowling at ticker tape, testing mashie niblicks, and riffling through first editions. It may be only sexual chauvinism on my part, but I submit that the opportunities for merchandising male lingerie are limitless. I offer at least one of them in crude dramatic form to blaze a trail for future copywriters.

(*Scene: The consulting room of Dr. Terence Fitch, an eminent Park Avenue specialist. The furniture consists of a few costly, unusual pieces, such as a kidney-shaped writing desk, a pancreas-shaped chair, and a spleen-shaped* spittoon. As the curtain rises, Miss Mayo, the nurse, is at the telephone-shaped telephone.)

MISS MAYO (into phone)—Hello, Dr. Volney? . . . This is Miss Mayo at Dr. Fitch's office. The Doctor is forwarding you his analysis of Mr. Tichenor's underwear problems; you should have it in the morning. . . . Not at all.

(As she hangs up, Dr. Fitch enters, thoughtfully stroking his Vandyke beard. He is followed by Freedley, a haggard, middle-aged patient, knotting his tie.)

DR. FITCH—Sit down, Freedley. . . . Oh, this is Miss Mayo. She's a niece of the Mayo brothers, out West.

FREEDLEY (warily)—How do you do, Miss Mayo? I've read grand things about your uncles.

MISS MAYO—Not mine, you haven't. They've been in Folsom the last three years for breaking and entering. (She exits.)

DR. FITCH (seating himself)—All right now, Freedley, suppose you tell me your symptoms.

FREEDLEY—But I just told them to you.

DR. FITCH—You did?

FREEDLEY—Sure, not ten minutes ago.

DR. FITCH—Well, repeat them. (Angrily) You don't suppose I have time to listen to every crackpot who comes in here bleating about his troubles, do you?

FREEDLEY (humbly)—No, sir. Well, it's just that I have this stuffy, uncomfortable sensation all the time.

DR. FITCH—That's the way a head cold usually starts. (Scribbling) You're to take fifteen of these tablets forty

48

times a day, or forty of them fifteen times a day, whichever is more convenient.

FREEDLEY—It's not my nose or throat, Doctor. I get it mostly around the hips and the small of my back.

DR. FITCH (*testily*)—Of course, of course. That's where it's localized. Now, I also want you to get hold of a tonic. I forgot the name of it, but it's about thirty dollars a bottle. The clerk'll know.

FREEDLEY—Will I feel better after I take it?

DR. FITCH (*coldly*)—I'm a physician, Freedley, not an astrologer. If you want a horoscope, there's a gypsy tea-room over on Lexington Avenue.

FREEDLEY (*plaintively*)—Gee, Dr. Fitch, this thing's got me crazy. I can't keep my mind on my work—

DR. FITCH—Work? Humph. Most of my patients have private incomes. What do you do?

FREEDLEY—I'm with the Bayonne Bag & String Company—assistant office manager.

DR. FITCH—Getting along pretty well there?

FREEDLEY (*pitifully*)—I was until this started. Now Mr. Borvis keeps riding me. He says I'm like a person in a fog.

DR. FITCH—That bulging, oppressive condition—notice it mostly when you're sitting down, don't you?

FREEDLEY—Why, how on earth can you tell, Doctor?

DR. FITCH—We medical men have ways of knowing these things. (*Gravely*) Well, Freedley, I can help you, but only if you face the facts.

FREEDLEY (*quavering*)—W-what is it, sir?

DR. FITCH—Your union suit is too big for you.

49

FREEDLEY (*burying his face in his hands*)—Oh, my God!

DR. FITCH—There, there. Buck up, old man. We mustn't give up hope.

FREEDLEY (*whimpering*)—But you might be mistaken —it's just a diagnosis.

DR. FITCH (*sternly*)—The fluoroscope never lies, Freedley. When I looked at you in there a moment ago, I saw almost five yards of excess fabric bunched around the mid-section.

FREEDLEY (*wildly*)—It's bound to shrink after I send it to the laundry! Maybe Velma can take a tuck in it!

DR. FITCH—That's only an evasion. (*Pressing a button*) It's lucky you came to me in time. If the public only knew the annual toll exacted by ponderous, loosely fitting underwear—(*Miss Mayo enters*) Miss Mayo, get me a sterile union suit, size thirty-eight, porous-knit.

FREEDLEY (*licking his lips*)—What—what are you going to do?

DR. FITCH (*soothingly*)—Now, this won't hurt a bit. We'll just slip it on for size—

FREEDLEY—I won't! *I won't!* (*He cowers into a corner, flailing at Dr. Fitch and Miss Mayo as they close in on him. They pinion his arms tightly, thrust him into an adjoining dressing room, and fling the union suit after him.*)

MISS MAYO (*in a low voice*)—Do you think he's got a chance, Doctor?

DR. FITCH—Hard to say, poor bugger. Did you feel those enlarged folds of material on his back?

Miss Mayo—He may have a blanket and some sheets hidden on him.

Dr. Fitch—You can't tell. They get cunning in the later stages.

(*The door-shaped door of the dressing room opens and Freedley re-enters, a changed man. He is portly, well groomed, a connoisseur of fine horseflesh and pretty women, but withal a man of keen business judgment. He wears a pearl-gray Homburg, Chesterfield overcoat, and spats, carries a gold-headed cane, a hot bird, and a cold bottle.*)

Freedley (*booming*)—Well, Fitch, my boy, can't waste any more time jawing with you. I've got to cut along to that board meeting. Just merged Bayonne Bag & String with Consolidated Twine, you know!

Dr. Fitch—Er—that was rather sudden, wasn't it?

Freedley—Can't stand beating about the bush. Think in telegrams, that's my motto. Want to know my secret, Fitch? I've worked hard and I've played hard. And I've drunk a quart of whiskey every day of my life!

Dr. Fitch—Well, remember what I said. Don't overdo it.

Freedley (*roaring*)—Stuff and nonsense! Why, I'm as sound as a nut. Got the appetite of a boy of twenty, sleep like a top, and I'll outdance a youngster any day! (*To demonstrate, he catches up Miss Mayo, whirls her around giddily, and, flushed with exertion, drops dead. The Doctor and his nurse exchange slow, sidelong glances.*)

Miss Mayo—Well, I guess science still has a lot to learn.

DR. FITCH (curtly)—None of your god-damned lip. Drag him out and show in the next patient. (*He turns back to his desk, stroking his Vandyke more thoughtfully than ever.*)

CURTAIN

FROU-FROU, OR VERTIGO REVISITED

Just in case anybody here missed me at the Mermaid Tavern this afternoon when the bowl of sack was being passed, I spent most of it reclining on my chaise longue in a negligee trimmed with marabou, reading trashy bonbons and eating French yellow-backed novels. What between amnesia (inability to find my rubbers) and O'Hara's disease (ability to remember all the cunning things I did last night), you might think I'd have sense enough to sit still and mind my own business. But, oh, no, not I. I had to start looking through *Harper's Bazaar* yet.

If a perfectly strange lady came up to you on the street and demanded, "Why don't you travel with a little raspberry-colored cashmere blanket to throw over yourself in hotels and trains?" the chances are that you would turn on your heel with dignity and hit her with a bottle. Yet that is exactly what has been happening for the past twenty months in the pages of a little raspberry-colored magazine called *Harper's Bazaar*. And don't think it does any good to pretend there *is* no magazine called *Harper's Bazaar*. I've tried that, too, and all I get is something called "circular insanity." Imagine having both circular insanity and *Harper's Bazaar*!

The first time I noticed this "Why Don't You?" department was a year ago last August while hungrily devouring news of the midsummer openings in the *haute couture*. Without any preamble came the stinging query, "Why don't you rinse your blonde child's hair in dead

53

champagne, as they do in France? Or pat her face gently with cream before she goes to bed, as they do in England?" After a quick look into the nursery, I decided to let my blonde child go to hell her own way, as they do in America, and read on. "Why don't you," continued the author, spitting on her hands, "twist her pigtails around her ears like macaroons?" I reread this several times to make sure I wasn't dreaming and then turned to the statement of ownership in the back of the magazine. Just because the Marquis de Sade wasn't mentioned didn't fool me; you know as well as I do who must have controlled fifty-one per cent of the stock. I slept across the foot of the crib with a loaded horse pistol until the next issue appeared.

It appeared, all right, all right, and after a quick gander at the activities of Nicky de Gunzburg, Lady Abdy, and the Vicomtesse de Noailles, which left me right back where I started, I sought out my "Why Don't You?" column. "Why don't you try the effect of diamond roses and ribbons flat on your head, as Garbo wears them when she says good-bye to Armand in their country retreat?" asked Miss Sly Boots in a low, thrilling voice. I was living in my own country retreat at the time, and as it happened to be my day to go to the post office (ordinarily the post office comes to me), I welcomed this chance to vary the monotony. Piling my head high with diamond roses and ribbons, I pulled on a pair of my stoutest *espadrilles* and set off, my cat frisking ahead of me with many a warning cry of "Here comes my master, the Marquis of Carabas!" We reached the post office without incident, except for the elderly Amish woman hoeing cabbages in her garden As I threw her a cheery greeting, Goody Two-shoes looked up, gave a rapid exhibition of Cheyne-Stokes breathing, and immediately turned to stone. In case you ever get down that way, she is still standing there, slightly chipped but otherwise in very good condition, which is more than I can say for the postmaster. When I walked in, he was in process of spitting into the top drawer, where he keeps the money-order blanks. One look at Boxholder 14 and he went out the window without bothering to raise the sash. A second later I heard a frightened voice directing a small boy to run for the hex doctor next door to the Riegels'. I spent the night behind some willows near the Delaware and managed to work my way back to the farm without being detected, but it was a matter of months before I was able to convince the countryside that I had a twin brother, enormously wealthy but quite mad, who had eluded his guards and paid me a visit.

For a time I went on a sort of *Harper's Bazaar* wagon, tapering myself off on *Pictorial Review* and *Good Housekeeping*, but deep down I knew I was a gone goose. Whenever I got too near a newsstand bearing a current issue of the *Bazaar* and my head started to swim, I would rush home and bury myself in dress patterns. And then, one inevitable day, the dam burst. Lingering in Brentano's basement over *L'Illustration* and *Blanco y Negro*, I felt the delicious, shuddery, half-swooning sensation of being drawn into the orbit again. On a table behind me lay a huge stack of the very latest issue of *Harper's Bazaar*, smoking hot from the presses. "Ah, come on," I heard my evil genius whisper. "One little peek can't hurt you. Nobody's looking." With trembling fingers I fumbled through the advertisements for Afghan hounds, foundation garments, and bath foams to the "Why Don't You?" section. Tiny beads of perspiration stood out on my even tinier forehead as I began to read, "Why don't you build beside the sea, or in the center of your garden, a white summer dining room shaped like a tent, draped with wooden swags, with walls of screen and Venetian blinds, so you will be safe from bugs and drafts?" I recoiled, clawing the air. "No, no!" I screamed. "I won't! I can't! *Help!*" But already the column was coiling around me, its hot breath on my neck. "Why don't you concentrate on fur jackets of marvelous workmanship and cut, made of inexpensive furs with incomprehensible names? Why don't you bring back from Central Europe a huge white baroque porcelain stove to stand in your front hall, reflected in the parquet? Why don't you buy in a hardware store a plain pine knife-basket with two compartments and a handle—mount this on four legs and you will have the ideal little table to sort letters and bills on, and to carry from your bedside to the garden or wherever you happen to be?" Unfortunately I had only the two legs God gave me, but I mounted those basement stairs like a cheetah, fought off the restraining hands of voluptuous salesladies, and hurtled out into the cool, sweet air of West Forty-seventh Street. I'm sorry I snatched the paper knife out of that desk set, Mr. Brentano, but you can send a boy for it at my expense. And by the way, do you ever have any call for back numbers of fashion magazines?

SCENARIO

Fade in, exterior grassy knoll, long shot. Above the scene the thundering measures of Von Suppe's "Light Cavalry Overture." Austerlitz? The Plains of Abraham? Vicksburg? The Little Big Horn? Cambrai? Steady on, old son; it is Yorktown. Under a blood-red setting sun yon proud crest is Cornwallis. Blood and 'ouns, proud sirrah, dost brush so lightly past an exciseman of the Crown? Lady Rotogravure's powdered shoulders shrank from the highwayman's caress; what, Jermyn, footpads on Hounslow Heath? A certain party in the D. A.'s office will hear of this, you bastard. There was a silken insolence in his smile as he drew the greatcoat about his face and leveled his shooting-iron at her dainty puss. Leave go that lady or I'll smear yuh. No quarter, eh? Me, whose ancestors scuttled stately India merchantmen of their comfits and silken stuffs and careened their piratical craft in the Dry Tortugas to carouse with bumboat women till the cock crew? Yuh'll buy my booze or I'll give yuh a handful of clouds. Me, whose ancestors rode with Yancey, Jeb Stuart, and Joe Johnston through the dusty bottoms of the Chickamauga? Oceans of love, but not one cent for tribute. Make a heel out of a guy whose grandsire, Olaf Hasholem, swapped powder and ball with the murderous Sioux through the wheels of a Conestoga wagon, who mined the yellow dirt with Sutter and slapped nuggets across the rude bars of Leadville and Goldfield? One side, damn your black hide, suh, or Ah'll send one mo' dirty Litvak to the boneyard. It's right up the exhibitor's alley, Mr. Biberman, and you got to hand it to them on a platter steaming hot. I know, Stanley, but let's look at this thing reasonable; we been showing the public Folly Larrabee's drawers two years and they been cooling off. Jeez Crize— it's a hisTORical drama, Mr. Biberman, it'll blow 'em outa the back of the houses, it's the greatest thing in the industry, it's dynamite! Pardon me, officer, is that General Washington? Bless yer little heart, mum, and who may yez be, savin' yer prisince? Honest old Brigid the apple-woman of Trinity, is it? How dégagé he sits on his charger, flicking an infinitesimal speck of ash from his plum-colored waistcoat! Gentlemen, I give you Martha Custis, hetman of the Don Cossacks, her features etched with the fragile beauty of a cameo. And I walked right in on her before she had a chance to pull the god-damned kimono together. But to be away from all this—to lean back puffing on one's churchwarden at Mount Vernon amid the dull glint of pewter, to watch the firelight play· ing over polished Duncan Phyfe and Adam while faithful old Cudjo cackles his ebony features and mixes a steaming lime toddy! Tired, Roy, I'm tired, I tell you. Tired of the rain, the eternal surge of the breakers on that lagoon, the glitter of the reef in that eternity out there. CHRIS· TIAN! She laughed contemptuously, her voluptuous throat filling with a rising sob as she faced Davidson like a hounded animal. You drove me out of Papeete but I'll go to Thursday Island with my banjo on my knee. Yeh, yeh, so what? We made FOUR pictures like that last year. Oh, my God, Mr. Biberman, give me a chance, it's only a flashback to plant that she's a woman with a past. Sixteen hundred a week I pay you to hand me back the plot of *Love's Counterfeiters* Selig made in 1912! She's who? She's what? What's the idea her coming here? What's she trying to do, turn a production office into a whorehouse? No, Miss Reznick, tell her to wait, I'll be through in five minutes. Now get it, Mr. Biberman, it's big. You establish the messroom and truck with Farnsworth till he faces Charteris. I said Sixth Rajputana Rifles and I don't want a lotta muggs paradin' around in the uniforms of the Preobazhensky Guard, y' get me? Yep, he's on a tear, those foreign directors are very temperamental, did I ever tell you about the time Lazlo Nugasi said he'd buy me a brassiere if I let him put it on? Fake it with a transparency of Khyber Pass. Now an overhead shot of the dusty tired column filing into Sidi-bel-Abbes. Shoulder by shoulder they march in the faded blue of the Legion, fun-loving Dick and serious-minded Tom. Buddies, the greatest word in the French language, flying to the defense of each other like a homo pigeon. Greater love hath Onan. Swinging a chair into that mob of lime-juicers in the Mile End Bar in Shanghai. But came a slant-eyed Chinese adventuress, and then? Don't shoot, Butch, for Gossake! Heave 'em into the prison yard, we'll keep the screws out of the cell-block and wilderness were paradise enow. Stow the swag in Cincy, kid, and go on alone, I'm done for. Too late, old Pogo the clown stopped it in the sweetbreads. They buried him outside the town that night, a motley crew of freaks and circus people. What a sequence! Old man Klingspiel told me he bawled like a

59

baby. Laugh, you inhuman monster they call the crowd, old Pogo lies dead with only a bareback rider's spangle to mark his grave and a seat for every child in the public schools! When tall ships shook out their plumage and raced from Salem to Hong Kong to bring back tea. Break out the Black Ball ensign, Mr. Exhibitor, there's sweet music in that ole cash register! A double truck in every paper in town and a smashing drawing by the best artist we got, mind you. Take the kiddies to that colossal red-blooded human drama of a boy's love for his dog. This is my hunting lodge, we'll stop here and dry your things. But of course it's all right, cara mia, I'm old enough to be your father. Let me go, you beast—MOTHER! What are you doing here? I ask you confidentially, Horowitz, can't we get that dame to put on some women's clothes, a skirt or something? The fans are getting wise, all those flat-heeled shoes and men's shirts like a lumberjack. Get me Gerber in publicity, he'll dish out some crap about her happy home life. Vorkapich around the room to Dmitri's brother officers as they register consternation at the news. Good chance for some hokey bellies on comedy types. What, sir, you dare mention Alexandra Petrovna's name in a saloon? The kid takes it big and gives Diane the gloves across the pan socko. The usual satisfaction, I presume? Drawing on his gloves as a thin sneer played across his features. Yeh, a martinet and for Crisakes remember it's not a musical instrument this time. But eet ees madness, Serge! The best swordsman in St. Mary's parish, he weel run you through in a tweenkling! Oh, darling, you can't, you can't. Her hair had become undone and he plunged his face into its fragrance, unbuckling his sabre and flinging it on the bed beside them. Hurry, even now my husband is fried to the ears in a low boozing-den in Pokrovsky Street. Of course it is he, I'd know that lousy busby anywhere in St. Petersburg. Shoot it two ways, you can always dub it in the sound track. She shrieks or she don't shriek, what the hell difference does it make? Told me he was going to night school at the Smolny Institute, the cur. And I believed him, thought Pyotr pityingly, surveying her luscious bust with greedy eyes. Never leave me, my sweet, and then bejeezus an angle shot toward the door of the General leaning against the lintel stroking his mustache. Crouching against the wall terrified yet shining-eyed as women are when men do gallant combat. Throw him your garter, Lady Aspinwall, throw your slipper, throw your lunch, but for Gawd's sake throw something! *Parry! Thrust! Touché!* Where are they all now, the old familiar faces? What a piece of business! Grabs a string of onions and swings himself up the balcony, fencing with the soldiers. Got you in the groin that time, General! Mine host, beaming genially, rubbing his hands and belching. Get Anderson ready with the sleighbells and keep that snow moving. Hit 'em all! Hotter on eighty-four, Joe Devlin! Are we up to speed? Quiet, please, we're turning! Chicago, hog-butcher to the world, yclept the Windy City. BOOZE AND BLOOD, he oughta know, running a drug store eleven years on Halstead Street. You cut to the back of the Big Fellow, then three lap dissolves of the presses—give 'em that Ufa stuff, then to the street— a newsbody, insert of the front page, the L roaring by—

Kerist, it's the gutsiest thing in pictures! Call you back, chief. Never mind the Hays office, this baby is censor-proof! Call you back, chief. We'll heave the telephone through the glass door and smack her in the kisser with the grapefruit, they liked it once and they'll love it twice. Call you back, chief. The gat in the mesh-bag. A symbol, get me? Now remember, staccato. . . A bit tight, my sweet? Marrowforth teetered back and forth on his heels, his sensitive artist's fingers caressing the first edition he loved. Item, one Hawes and Curtis dress-suit, one white tie, kindly return to Mister Dreyfus in the wardrobe depart-ment. What color do I remind you of? Purple shot with pleasure, if you ask me. Do I have to work with a lot of pim-ply grips giving me the bird? Papa's in the doghouse and keep up the tempo of the last scene, you looked crummy in yesterday's dailies. A warm, vivid and human story with just that touch of muff the fans demand. Three Hundred Titans Speed Westward as King Haakon Lays Egg on Shoe-String. And sad-eyed Grubnitz by the Wailing Wall demands: What will the inde exhibs do? Let 'em eat cake, we're packing 'em in with 29 Garson-Pidgeons in 1944. Ask Hyman Gerber of Waco, he can smell a box-office pic-ture a mile away. In the freezing mists of dawn they gath-ered by the fuselages of their planes and gripped hands. But Rex Jennings of the shining eyes and the high heart never came back. Jerry got him over Chalons. I tell you it's murder to send a mere boy up in a crate like that! The god-damned production office on my neck all day. It's midsummer madness, Fiametta! You mustn't! I must! I want you! You want me? But I—I'm just a poor little slavey, and you—why, all life's ahead of you! Fame, the love of a good woman, children! And your music, Raoul! Excuse me, miss, are you Fiametta Desplains? I am Yankel Patchouli, a solicitor. Here is my card and a report of my recent urinalysis. Raoul! Raoul! Come quick! A million dollars! Now you can go to Paris and study your counterpoint! Damn my music, Fiametta, my happiness was in my own back yard all the time and I was, how you say it, one blind fool. The gingham dress and half-parted lips leaning on a broom. But why are you looking at me in that strange way, Tony? . . . Tony! I'm afraid of you! Oh . . . You utter contemptible despicable CAD. He got up nursing his jaw. Spew out your poison, you rat. You didn't know she was the morganatic wife of Prince Rupprecht, *did* you? That her affairs with men were the talk of Vienna, *did* you? That—Vanya, is this true? Bowed head, for her man. His boyish tousled head clean-cut against the twilight. Get out. *Get out.* GET OUT! Oh, mumsey, I want to die. That hooker's gotta lay off that booze, Mr. Metz, once more she comes on the set stinking and I take the next boat back to Buda-Pesth. But in a great tangled garden sits a forlorn tragic-eyed figure; the face a mask of carved ivory, the woman nobody knows—Tilly Bergstrom. What lies behind her shattered romance with Grant Snavely, idol of American flaps? Turn 'em over, you punks, I'll stay on this set till I get it right. Cheese it, de nippers! The jig is up, long live the jig—ring out the old, ring in the new. For love belongs to everyone, the best things in life are free.

A FAREWELL TO OMSK

(*The terrifying result of reading an entire gift set of Dostoievsky in one afternoon.*)

Late one afternoon in January, 18—, passersby in L. Street in the town of Omsk might have seen a curious sight. A young man of a somewhat flushed, feverish appearance was standing outside Pyotr Pyotrvitch's tobacco shop. This in itself was interesting, as Pyotr Pyotrvitch had no tobacco shop in L. Street. Even had he had one, there would have been a large gaping hole in the sidewalk in front of it due to a sewer excavation, so that only the top of the young man's head would be visible. Of itself there was nothing unusual in the spectacle of a young man standing up to his knees in water staring fixedly at the fresh loam piled up about him. What amused the passersby was that any one should want to go into Pyotr Pyotrvitch's shop, since it was common knowledge that Pyotr had died some years before of the bends and his shop had been converted into an abattoir or worse. Indeed, there were those who maintained that the shop had never been there at all—was, in short, a sort of mirage such as is often seen by travelers in the desert. But there was such a look of idealism on the young man's face, of the kind which is so often to be observed nowadays in our Russian university students, that the irreverent titters and cries of "Ach, pfoo!" were quickly silenced. Finally the young man sighed deeply, cast a look of determination around him, and entered the shop.

"Good afternoon, Pyotr Pyotrvitch!" he said resolutely.

"Good afternoon, Afya Afyakievitch!" replied the shopkeeper warmly. He was the son of a former notary public attached to the household of Prince Grashkin and gave himself no few airs in consequence. Whilst speaking it was his habit to extract a greasy barometer from his waistcoat and consult it importantly, a trick he had learned from the Prince's barber. On seeing Afya Afyakievitch he skipped about nimbly, dusted off the counter, gave one of his numerous offspring a box on the ear, drank a cup of tea, and on the whole behaved like a man of the world who has affairs of moment occupying him.

"Well, Afya Afyakievitch," he said with a sly smile, "what can I sell you today? Cigarettes, perhaps?"

"Cigarettes?" repeated the young man vaguely. A peculiar shudder passed over his frame as he regarded the top of Pyotr's head intently. It was just wide enough to fit the blade of an ax. A strange smile played about his lips, and only the entrance of another personage distracted him. This was none other than Alaunia Alaunovna, the shopkeeper's daughter, a prostitute with a look of exaltation on her timid face, who entered and stood unobtrusively in a corner.

"How patient she is!" thought the young man, his heart touched. An overpowering desire to throw himself at her feet and kiss the hem of her garment filled his being.

"Well, well!" exclaimed Pyotr Pyotrvitch, anxious to impress his customer. "Allow me, kind sir, to present my daughter, Alaunia Alaunovna. She is a girl of education— he, he!" A stifling feeling overcame the young man; he wanted to throw himself at the man's feet and bite them.

Alaunia Alaunovna dropped a small curtsy. The young man, a pitying expression on his face, picked it up and quickly returned it to her. She gave him a grateful glance named Joe.

"And—and what does your daughter do?" Afya asked with emotion.

"She is a prostitute in a small way of business," replied Pyotr proudly.

"It's great work if you can get it," the young man stammered.

"Permit me, it is the only way to live!" cried the shopkeeper excitedly. But by now Afya was even more excited than he was.

"Ah yes—excuse me—that is to say!" he began confusedly. A swarm of thoughts filled his brain. "I used to know a man, a titular councilor, Andron Andronovitch Pojarsky, in the province of Z——. We were in the Gymnasium together. Well, only fancy, last night I met him at the Petrovsky Bridge, as I was returning from Dunya's where we were having a discussion of certain ideas, I won't go into them, but Pimentov—he is a good-hearted fellow, he had entered into a free marriage with his cousin —tfoo, how I wander! Well, this Andron Andronovitch, poor fellow, is in a bad way, in a word is reduced to eating his rubbers, all he has left, in a certain sense. Ach, these Slavophiles!" broke off Afya, taking out some old pieces of cucumber and fish he had been carrying in his pocket and dipping them in his tea. "Just imagine, he has such extreme notions—Utopias, one might say. . . ."

"Yes! Yes!" interrupted Pyotr, nodding with great

rapidity, almost perspiring with excitement. "But you spoke formerly of cigarettes, did you not? Here is a good brand—fifteen kopecks a package, or two packages for twenty-five kopecks! A brand much favored by the garrison, young gentleman!"

"Fifteen kopecks?" asked Afya slowly. "Then the second package must be only ten kopecks?"

"True, young sir," said Pyotr, screwing up his little red-rimmed eyes in the manner of one who is about to inspect a private aquarium. "But unfortunately I have only one package."

"Pyotr Pyotrvitch," said the young man quietly, "do you know what I think? I think this is a hell of a tobacco shop, in any language."

"You're telling *me*?" inquired Pyotr sadly. "Hey, where are you going? Just a moment—come, a cup of tea—let's have a discussion. . . ."

"I'll be right outside in that sewer excavation if you want me," said Afya over his shoulder. "I'd sort of like to brood over things for a while."

"Well, skip the gutter," sighed Pyotr.

"Don't take any flannel kopecks," said Afya gloomily. He dislodged a piece of horse-radish from his tie, shied it at a passing Nihilist, and slid forward into the fresh loam.

NOTHING BUT THE TOOTH

I am thirty-eight years old, have curly brown hair and blue eyes, own a uke and a yellow roadster, and am considered a snappy dresser in my crowd. But the thing I want most in the world for my birthday is a free subscription to *Oral Hygiene*, published by Merwin B. Massol, 1005 Liberty Avenue, Pittsburgh, Pa. In the event you have been repairing your own teeth, *Oral Hygiene* is a respectable smooth-finish technical magazine circulated to your dentist with the compliments of his local supply company. Through its pages runs a recital of the most horrendous and fantastic deviations from the dental norm. It is a confessional in which dentists take down their back hair and stammer out the secrets of their craft. But every time I plunge into its crackling pages at my dentist's, just as I get interested in the story of the Man with the Alveolar Dentures or Thirty Reasons Why People Stay Away from Dentists, the nurse comes out slightly flushed and smoothing her hair to tell me that the doctor is ready. Last Thursday, for example, I was head over heels in the question-and-answer department of *Oral Hygiene*. A frankly puzzled extractionist, who tried to cloak his agitation under the initials "J. S. G.," had put his plight squarely up to the editor: "I have a patient, a woman of 20, who has a full complement of teeth. All of her restorations are gold foils or inlays. She constantly grinds her teeth at night. How can I aid her to stop grinding them? Would it do any good to give her a vellum rubber bite?"

68

But before I could learn whether it was a bite or just a gentle hug the editor recommended, out popped Miss Inchbald with lipstick on her nose, giggling, "The Doctor is free now." "Free" indeed—"running amok" would be a better way to put it.

I had always thought of dentists as of the phlegmatic type—square-jawed sadists in white aprons who found release in trying out new kinds of burs on my shaky little incisors. One look at *Oral Hygiene* fixed that. Of all the inhibited, timorous, uncertain fumble-bunnies who creep the earth, Mr. Average Dentist is the worst. A filing clerk is a veritable sabre-toothed tiger by comparison. Faced with a decision, your dentist's bones turn to water and he becomes all hands and feet. He muddles through his ordinary routine with a certain amount of bravado, plugging a molar here with chewing gum, sinking a shaft in a sound tooth there. In his spare time he putters around his laboratory making tiny cement cup-cakes, substituting amber electric bulbs for ordinary bulbs in his waiting-room to depress patients, and jotting down nasty little innuendoes about people's gums in his notebook. But let an honest-to-goodness sufferer stagger in with his face out of drawing, and Mr. Average Dentist's nerves go to hell. He runs sobbing to the "Ask *Oral Hygiene*" department and buries his head in the lap of V. C. Smedley, its director. I dip in for a typical sample:

Question—A patient of mine, a girl, 18, returned from school recently with a weird story of lightning having struck an upper right cuspid tooth and checked the enamel on the labial surface nearly two-thirds of the way from the incisal edge toward the neck. The patient was lying on a bed looking out an open window during an electric storm, and this one flash put out the lights of the house, and at the same time, the patient felt a burning sensation (like a burning wire) along the cuspid tooth. She immediately put her tongue on the tooth which felt rough, but as the lights were out she could not see it so she went to bed. (A taste as from a burnt match accompanied the shock.)

Next morning she found the labial of the tooth black. Some of the color came off on her finger. By continually brushing all day with the aid of peroxide, salt, soda and vinegar she removed the remainder of the black after which the tooth was a yellow shade and there was some roughness on the labial surface.

Could the lightning have caused this and do you recommend smoothing the surface with discs?—R. D. L., D.D.S., Oregon.

Well, Doctor, let us take your story step by step. Miss Muffet told you the sensation was like a burning wire, and she tasted something like a burnt match. Did you think, by any chance, of looking into her mouth for either wire or matches? Did you even think of looking into her mouth? I see no mention of the fact in your letter. You state that she walked in and told you the story, that's all. Of course it never occurred to you that she had brought along her mouth for a reason. Then you say, "she removed the remainder of the black after which the tooth was a yellow shade." Would it be asking too much of you to make up your mind? Was it a tooth or a yellow shade? You're quite sure it wasn't a Venetian blind? Or a gaily striped awning? Do you ever take a drink in the daytime, Doctor?

Frankly, men, I have no patience with such idiotic professional behavior. An eighteen-year-old girl walks into a dentist's office exhibiting obvious symptoms of religious hysteria (stigmata, etc.). She babbles vaguely of thunderstorms and is patently a confirmed drunkard. The dentist goes to pieces, forgets to look in her mouth, and scurries off to *Oral Hygiene* asking for permission to smooth her surface with discs. It's a mercy he doesn't take matters into his own hands and try to plough every fourth tooth under. This is the kind of man to whom we intrust our daughters' dentures.

There is practically no problem so simple that it cannot confuse a dentist. For instance, thumb-sucking. "Could you suggest a method to correct thumb and index finger sucking by an infant of one year?" flutters a Minnesota orthodontist, awkwardly digging his toe into the hot sand. Dr. Smedley, whose patience rivals Job's, has an answer for everything: "Enclose the hand by tying shut the end of the sleeve of a sleeping garment, or fasten a section of a pasteboard mailing tube to the sleeping garment in such a position as to prevent the bending of the elbow sufficiently to carry the thumb or index finger to the mouth." Now truly, Dr. Smedley, isn't that going all the way around Robin Hood's barn? Nailing the baby's hand to the highchair is much more cozy, or, if no nail is available, a smart blow with the hammer on Baby's fingers will slow him down. My grandfather, who was rather active in the nineties (between Columbus and Amsterdam Avenues—they finally got him for breaking and entering), always used an effective method to break children of this habit,

He used to tie a Mills grenade to the baby's thumb with cobbler's waxed thread, and when the little spanker pulled out the detonating pin with his teeth, Grandpa would stuff his fingers into his ears and run like the wind. Ironically enough, the people with whom Grandpa now boards have the same trouble keeping him from biting his thumbs, but overcome it by making him wear a loose jacket with very long sleeves, which they tie to the bars.

I have always been the mildest of men, but you remember the old saying, "Beware the fury of a patient man." (I remembered it very well and put my finger on it instantly, page 269 of Bartlett's book of quotations.) For years I have let dentists ride rough-shod over my teeth; I have been sawed, hacked, chopped, whittled, bewitched, bewildered, tattooed, and signed on again; but this is cuspid's last stand. They'll never get me into that chair again. I'll dispose of my teeth as I see fit, and after they're gone, I'll get along. I started off living on gruel, and, by God, I can always go back to it again.

WOODMAN,
DON'T SPARE THAT TREE!

Not long ago a landscape architect down my way was retained by a lady who, to put it bluntly, had just fallen heir to a satchelful of the stuff. Instead of the same old flowers and trees, the fair client wanted a garden plan for her country house which would express her own unique personality: something arresting, terribly audacious, yet smart; in short, identifying her unmistakably as a lady who had just fallen heir to a satchelful. The architect smacked his lips in a refined way, like a fox in a henhouse, and went to work. Employing a dozen wooden horses gleaned from a defunct amusement park, and a profusion of the rarest vines, creepers, and bulbs known to man, he created a spectacular floral carrousel that dazzled the countryside. Farmers came from miles around to lean on their manure forks and gape at the horticultural gew-gaw, but Mrs. Krebs was clearly disappointed.

"You haven't captured my mood at all," she pouted. "Deep down, I'm really a mystic—haunting, inscrutable. Now this," she went on, waving toward a mournful Chirico which had set her back eleven thousand clams, "this is really *me*."

"You took the words right out of my mouth," agreed the architect, "but I was just interpreting the little girl in you. The spiritual side is on the fire and should be ready any day now."

A week later, wrenched from its native California by political influence plus considerable baksheesh, a gnarled

Monterey cypress rolled into the county seat on a flatcar. It was unloaded and borne to the estate, where a gang of workmen sank it in a cement base and sprayed it dead white. One of New York's most recherché decorators then looped smilax and Spanish moss from its writhing limbs, and on the first night of the full moon the result was unveiled to its owner. The effect was so electric that the architect now sends his fees to the bank in an armored car and has taken to wearing pencil-striped pants in the forenoon.

One might be inclined to shrug one's pretty shoulders and dismiss such decadence as isolated were it not for a photograph in a recent issue of the *American Home*. It portrays a lifeless apple tree, hairy with vines and birdbaths, rearing up forlornly in a small patio under the caption "Seeing the artistic possibilities of this dead tree, Mrs. Clyde L. Hagerman, of Bloomfield Hills, Michigan, bought it, had it set in concrete in her outdoor living room, so she can drape it each summer in moon-flowers and gourd vines." Here, then, is a trend, as significant as the first shifter pin or the original Eugénie hat. As the hysteria spreads, any number of provocative situations may arise, but one of them seems to fall naturally into the dramatic pattern. Places, please.

(*Scene: A country road toward dusk. A station wagon rounds the bend, in its front seat Mr. and Mrs. Updegraff. The tonneau is heaped high with Chinese-lacquer taborets inlaid with mother-of-pearl, paintings on velvet, and other post-Victorian bagatelles with which Mrs. Updegraff plans to redecorate her home. She is busily examining two yellowed Welsbach mantles.)*

MRS. UPDEGRAFF (*exultantly*)—They're just like the ones Lilian Gassaway bought at the Parke-Bernet Galleries—she'll be furious! I'll have them dyed dark blue and use them for flower-holders.

MR. UPDEGRAFF (*listlessly*)—What are you going to do with that old sewing machine back there—open a sweat-shop?

MRS. UPDEGRAFF—No, the feet'll make a lovely coffee table. I saw the very piece of marble in that Portuguese cemetery we passed. Couldn't we sneak out some dark night . . .

MR. UPDEGRAFF (*violently*)—Who the hell do you think we are—Burke and Hare? Now, listen, look here, Juanita—

MRS. UPDEGRAFF (*suddenly*)—Stop! Stop the car! We just passed it!

MR. UPDEGRAFF—What?

MRS. UPDEGRAFF—The hickory I've been lickory for—I mean the hickory I've been looking for! Oh, Leslie, it's a dream! Look at those great, tormented limbs! Come on! Let's find out how much they're asking!

MR. UPDEGRAFF (*desperately*)—Now, Juanita, you know we can't afford—

MRS. UPDEGRAFF (*in another world*)—I can just see Myrtle Greneker's face, giving herself airs with that miserable little sycamore of hers.

MR. UPDEGRAFF—But this thing's dead!

75

Mrs. Updegraff—Of course it is, silly. Do you suppose I'd put a live hickory in our patio? Don't be tacky.

Mr. Updegraff—A zombie, that's what I married. Cemeteries, dead hickories. . . .

(He moodily throws the car into reverse. The curtain is lowered for a few moments while the scenery is being shifted. Should the audience become restive, the interval can be filled by a ballet, "Six Who Pass While the Concrete Boils," in which half a dozen stocky Bryn Mawr girls in gray jersey stride convulsively from one end of the stage to the other tugging at a veil. This symbolizes the forces of water, sand, and Portland cement at first refusing to work harmoniously, then uniting for the common good. When the curtain rises again it discloses Reuben Hayseed, a farmer with chin whiskers and a linen duster, seated in a rocker tilted against his home, over which towers the dead hickory. One of Reuben's two young sons has hoisted his brother up into the limbs in a fragile box of the sort used for packing eggs.)

Hayseed (thickly)—Gad, it's murder to send a mere boy up in a crate like that.

(His words are prophetic; a moment later the boy plummets out of the tree and breaks his neck. He is borne off stage with many lamentations by the six Bryn Mawr girls in a pageant entitled "Youth in the Hands of the Receivers." Enter Mr. and Mrs. Updegraff.)

Mrs. Updegraff—That tree's unsafe! It ought to be condemned!

Hayseed (*placidly*)—We like it.

Mrs. Updegraff—You watch, it'll come crashing down through the roof some day.

Hayseed—That's what makes life at Echo Valley Farm so piquant.

Mrs. Updegraff (*snorting*)—It's just a lot of old firewood to me.

Hayseed—Really? I can't quite agree. Sometimes, viewed by moonlight, its gaunt agony typifies the melancholy and futility of existence.

Mr. Updegraff—That's pretty dickty talk for a farmer.

Hayseed—It may interest you to learn that I am one of the few farmers who ever graduated from the Sorbonne.

Mr. Updegraff—No kid? Why, I'm an old Sorbonne man myself! What'd you major in?

Hayseed—None of your god-damned business.

Mrs. Updegraff—Look here, young man, we may have a use for that old stump. How much do you want for it?

Hayseed—Sixty dollars.

Mr. Updegraff—Sixty dollars!

Hayseed—Hear that echo? Clear as a bell. (*Proudly*) No wonder they call this place Echo Valley Farm.

Mrs. Updegraff—Isn't—isn't that rather expensive?

Hayseed—Not for an original. I've got a barnful of copies out there at ten dollars, if that's what you want.

Mrs. Updegraff—No, I couldn't bear anything near me that wasn't authentic. I'm funny that way.

Hayseed—So am I. I'd just as soon take half the money to have my pieces go into a home where they're appreciated.

Mr. Updegraff—Is that an offer?

Hayseed—No, simply a manner of speaking.

Mrs. Updegraff—Oh, Leslie, it *is* divine, isn't it? After all, we could economize next month. Spaghetti's cheap, but it's filling.

Mr. Updegraff (*a dead pigeon*)—Yes, dear. (*To Hayseed*) Do you mind taking a check? It isn't certified.

Hayseed—Not at all. What bank?

Mr. Updegraff—Corn Exchange.

Hayseed—Funny, I'm an old Corn Exchange man myself. How big's your balance?

Mr. Updegraff—None of your god-damned business.

Hayseed (*folding check*)—There. And now can I interest you folks in a plate of Mrs. Hayseed's real country doughnuts, piping hot from the oven?

Mr. Updegraff (*hastily*)—Er—no, thanks, we'll just pick up some cheap copies along the road.

(*As the Updegraffs exit, Hayseed resumes his seat in the rocker with a contented sigh and, taking up an old cobbler's bench, begins to convert it into a lamp.*)

CURTAIN

STRICTLY FROM HUNGER

Yes I was excited, and small wonder. What boy wouldn't be, boarding a huge, mysterious, puffing steam train for golden California? As Mamma adjusted my reefer and strapped on my leggings, I almost burst with impatience. Grinning redcaps lifted my luggage into the compartment and spat on it. Mamma began to weep into a small pillow-case she had brought along for the purpose.

"Oh, son, I wish you hadn't become a scenario writer!" she sniffled.

"Aw, now, Moms," I comforted her, "it's no worse than playing the piano in a call-house." She essayed a brave little smile, and, reaching into her reticule, produced a flat package which she pressed into my hands. For a moment I was puzzled, then I cried out with glee.

"Jelly sandwiches! Oh, Moms!"

"Eat them all, boy o' mine," she told me, "they're good for boys with hollow little legs." Tenderly she pinned to my lapel the green tag reading "To Plushnick Productions, Hollywood, California." The whistle shrilled and in a moment I was chugging out of Grand Central's dreaming spires followed only by the anguished cries of relatives who would now have to go to work. I had chugged only a few feet when I realized that I had left without the train, so I had to run back and wait for it to start.

As we sped along the glorious fever spots of the Hudson I decided to make a tour of inspection. To my surprise I found that I was in the only passenger car of the train; the other cars were simply dummies snipped out of cardboard and painted to simulate coaches. Even "passengers" had been cunningly drawn in colored crayons in the "window," as well as ragged tramps clinging to the blinds below and drinking Jamaica ginger. With a rueful smile I returned to my seat and gorged myself on jelly sandwiches.

At Buffalo the two other passengers and I discovered to our horror that the conductor had been left behind. We finally decided to divide up his duties; I punched the tickets, the old lady opposite me wore a conductor's hat and locked the washroom as we came into stations, and the young man who looked as if his feet were not mates consulted a Hamilton watch frequently. But we missed the conductor's earthy conversation and it was not until we had exchanged several questionable stories that we began to forget our loss.

A flicker of interest served to shorten the trip. At Fort Snodgrass, Ohio, two young and extremely polite road-agents boarded the train and rifled us of our belongings. They explained that they were modern Robin Hoods and were stealing from the poor to give to the rich. They had intended to rape all the women and depart for Sherwood Forest, but when I told them that Sherwood Forest as well as the women were in England, their chagrin was comical in the extreme. They declined my invitation to stay and take a chance on the train's pool, declaring that the engineer had fixed the run and would fleece us, and got off at South Bend with every good wish.

The weather is always capricious in the Middle West,

and although it was midsummer, the worst blizzard in Chicago's history greeted us on our arrival. The streets were crowded with thousands of newsreel cameramen trying to photograph one another bucking the storm on the Lake Front. It was a novel idea for the newsreels and I wished them well. With only two hours in Chicago I would be unable to see the city, and the thought drew me into a state of composure. I noted with pleasure that a fresh coat of grime had been given to the Dearborn Street station, though I was hardly vain enough to believe that it had anything to do with my visit. There was the usual ten-minute wait while the porters withdrew with my portable typewriter to a side room and flailed it with hammers, and at last I was aboard the "Sachem," crack train of the B.B.D. & O. lines.

It was as if I had suddenly been transported into another world. "General Crook," in whom I was to make my home for the next three days, and his two neighbors, "Lake Tahoe" and "Chief Malomai," were everything that the word "Pullman" implies; they were Pullmans. Uncle Eben, in charge of "General Crook," informed me that the experiment of air-cooling the cars had been so successful that the road intended trying to heat them next winter.

"Ah suttinly looks fo'd to dem roastin' ears Ah's gwine have next winter, he, he, he!" he chuckled, rubbing soot into my hat.

The conductor told me he had been riding on trains for so long that he had begun to smell like one, and sure enough, two brakemen waved their lanterns at him that night and tried to tempt him down a siding in Kansas City. We became good friends and it came as something of a blow when I heard the next morning that he had fallen off the train during the night. The fireman said that we had circled about for an hour trying to find him but that it had been impossible to lower a boat because we did not carry a boat.

The run was marked by only one incident out of the ordinary. I had ordered breaded veal cutlet the first evening, and my waiter, poking his head into the kitchen, had repeated the order. The cook, unfortunately, understood him to say "dreaded veal cutlet," and resenting the slur, sprang at the waiter with drawn razor. In a few seconds I was the only living remnant of the shambles, and at Topeka I was compelled to wait until a new shambles was hooked on and I proceeded with dinner.

It seemed only a scant week or ten days before we were pulling into Los Angeles. I had grown so attached to my porter that I made him give me a lock of his hair. I wonder if he still has the ten-cent piece I gave him? There was a gleam in his eye which could only have been insanity as he leaned over me. Ah, Uncle Eben, faithful old retainer, where are you now? Gone to what obscure ossuary? If this should chance to meet your kindly gaze, drop me a line care of Variety, won't you? They know what to do with it.

— II —

The violet hush of twilight was descending over Los Angeles as my hostess, Violet Hush, and I left its suburbs headed toward Hollywood. In the distance a glow of huge piles of burning motion-picture scripts lit up the sky. The crisp tang of frying writers and directors whetted my appetite. How good it was to be alive, I thought, inhaling deep lungfuls of carbon monoxide. Suddenly our powerful Gatti-Cazazza slid to a stop in the traffic.

"What is it, Jenkin?" Violet called anxiously through the speaking-tube to the chauffeur (played by Lyle Talbot).

A *suttee* was in progress by the roadside, he said—did we wish to see it? Quickly Violet and I elbowed our way through the crowd. An enormous funeral pyre composed of thousands of feet of film and scripts, drenched with Chanel Number Five, awaited the torch of Jack Holt, who was to act as master of ceremonies. In a few terse words Violet explained this unusual custom borrowed from the Hindus and never paid for. The worst disgrace that can befall a producer is an unkind notice from a New York reviewer. When this happens, the producer becomes a pariah in Hollywood. He is shunned by his friends, thrown into bankruptcy, and like a Japanese electing hara-kiri, he commits *suttee*. A great bonfire is made of the film, and the luckless producer, followed by directors, actors, technicians, and the producer's wives, immolate themselves. Only the scenario writers are exempt. These are tied between the tails of two spirited Caucasian ponies, which are then driven off in opposite directions. This custom is called "a conference."

Violet and I watched the scene breathlessly. Near us Harry Cohn, head of Columbia Studios, was being rubbed with huck towels preparatory to throwing himself into the flames. He was nonchalantly smoking a Rocky Ford five-center, and the man's courage drew a tear to the eye of even the most callous. Weeping relatives besought him to eschew his design, but he stood adamant. Adamant Eve, his plucky secretary, was being rubbed with crash towels preparatory to flinging herself into Cohn's embers. Assistant directors busily prepared spears, war-bonnets and bags of pemmican which the Great Chief would need on his trip to the "Happy Hunting Grounds." Wampas and beads to placate the Great Spirit (played by Will Hays) were piled high about the stoical tribesman.

Suddenly Jack Holt (played by Edmund Lowe) raised his hand for silence. The moment had come. With bowed head Holt made a simple invocation couched in one-syllable words so that even the executives might understand. Throwing his five-center to a group of autograph-hunters, the great man poised himself for the fatal leap. But from off-scene came the strident clatter of cocoanut shells, and James Agee, Filmdom's fearless critic, wearing the uniform of a Confederate guerrilla and the whiskers of General Beauregard, galloped in on a foam-flecked pinto. It was he whose mocking review had sent Cohn into Coventry. It was a dramatic moment as the two stood pitted against each other—Cohn against Agee, the Blue against the Gray. But with true Southern gallantry Agee was the first to extend the hand of friendship.

"Ah reckon it was an unworthy slur, suh," he said in manly tones. "Ah-all thought you-all's pictuah was lousy but it opened at the Rialto to sensational grosses, an'

Ah-all 'pologizes. Heah, have a yam." And he drew a yam from his tunic. Not to be outdone in hospitality, Cohn drew a yam from his tunic, and soon they were exchanging yams and laughing over the old days.

When Violet and I finally stole away to our waiting motor, we felt that we were somehow nearer to each other. I snuggled luxuriously into the buffalo lap-robe Violet had provided against the treacherous night air and gazed out at the gleaming neon lights. Soon we would be in Beverly Hills, and already the quaint native women were swarming alongside in their punts urging us to buy their cunning beadwork and mangoes. Occasionally I threw a handful of coppers to the Negro boys, who dove for them joyfully. The innocent squeals of the policemen as the small blackamoors pinched them were irresistible. Unable to resist them, Violet and I were soon pinching each other till our skins glowed. Violet was good to the touch, with a firm fleshy texture like a winesap or pippin. It seemed but a moment before we were sliding under the porte-cochère of her home, a magnificent rambling structure of beaverboard patterned after an Italian ropewalk of the sixteenth century. It had recently been remodeled by a family of wrens who had introduced chewing-gum into the left wing, and only three or four obscure Saxon words could do it justice.

I was barely warming my hands in front of the fire and watching Jimmy Fidler turn on a spit when my presence on the Pacific Slope made itself felt. The news of my arrival had thrown international financial centers into an uproar, and sheaves of wires, cables, phone messages, and even corn began piling up. An ugly rumor that I might reorganize the motion-picture industry was being bruited about in the world's commodity markets. My brokers, Whitelipped & Trembling, were beside themselves. The New York Stock Exchange was begging them for assurances of stability and Threadneedle Street awaited my next move with drumming pulses. Film shares ricocheted sharply, although wools and meats were sluggish, if not downright sullen. To the reporters who flocked around me I laughingly disclaimed that this was a business trip. I was simply a scenario writer to whom the idea of work was abhorrent. A few words murmured into the transatlantic telephone, the lift of an eyebrow here, the shrug of a shoulder there, and equilibrium was soon restored. I washed sparsely, curled my mustache with a heated hairpin, flicked a drop of Sheik Lure on my lapel, and rejoined my hostess.

After a copious dinner, melting-eyed beauties in lacy black underthings fought with each other to serve me kümmel. A hurried apology, and I was curled up in bed with the Autumn, 1927, issue of *The Yale Review*. Halfway through an exciting symposium on Sir Thomas Aquinas' indebtedness to Professors Whitehead and Spengler, I suddenly detected a stowaway blonde under the bed. Turning a deaf ear to her heartrending entreaties and burning glances, I sent her packing. Then I treated my face to a feast of skin food, buried my head in the pillow and went bye-bye.

Hollywood Boulevard! I rolled the rich syllables over on my tongue and thirstily drank in the beauty of the scene before me. On all sides nattily attired boulevardiers clad in rich stuffs strolled nonchalantly, inhaling cubebs and exchanging epigrams stolen from Martial and Wilde. Thousands of scantily draped but none the less appetizing extra girls milled past me, their mouths a scarlet wound and their eyes clearly defined in their faces. Their voluptuous curves set my blood on fire, and as I made my way down Mammary Lane, a strange thought began to invade my brain: I realized that I had not eaten breakfast yet. In a Chinese eatery cunningly built in the shape of an old shoe I managed to assuage the inner man with a chopped glove salad topped off with frosted cocoa. Charming platinum-haired hostesses in red pajamas and peaked caps added a note of color to the surroundings, whilst a gypsy orchestra played selections from Victor Herbert's operettas on musical saws. It was a bit of old Vienna come to life, and the sun was a red ball in the heavens before I realized with a start that I had promised to report at the Plushnick Studios.

Commandeering a taxicab, I arrived at the studio just in time to witness the impressive ceremony of changing the guard. In the central parade ground, on a snowy white charger, sat Max Plushnick, resplendent in a producer's uniform, his chest glittering with first mortgage liens, amortizations, and estoppels. His personal guard, composed of picked vice-presidents of the Chase National

Bank, was drawn up stiffly about him in a hollow square.

But the occasion was not a happy one. A writer had been caught trying to create an adult picture. The drums rolled dismally, and the writer, his head sunk on his chest, was led out amid a ghastly silence. With the aid of a small stepladder Plushnick slid lightly from his steed. Sternly he ripped the epaulets and buttons from the traitor's tunic, broke his sword across his knee, and in a few harsh words demoted him to the mail department.

"And now," began Plushnick, "I further condemn you to eat . . ."

"No, no!" screamed the poor wretch, falling to his knees and embracing Plushnick's jackboots, "not that, not that!"

"Stand up, man," ordered Plushnick, his lip curling, "I condemn you to eat in the studio restaurant for ten days and may God have mercy on your soul." The awful words rang out on the still evening air and even Plushnick's hardened old mercenaries shuddered. The heart-rending cries of the unfortunate were drowned in the boom of the sunset gun.

In the wardrobe department I was photographed, fingerprinted, and measured for the smock and Windsor tie which was to be my uniform. A nameless fear clutched at my heart as two impassive turnkeys herded me down a corridor to my supervisor's office. For what seemed hours we waited in an anteroom. Then my serial number was called, the leg-irons were struck off, and I was shoved through a door into the presence of Diana ffrench-Ma-moulian.

How to describe what followed? Diana ffrench-Mamou-lian was accustomed to having her way with writers, and my long lashes and peachblow mouth seemed to whip her to insensate desire. In vain, time and again, I tried to bring her attention back to the story we were discussing, only to find her gem-incrusted fingers straying through my hair. When our interview was over, her cynical attempt to "date me up" made every fiber of my being cry out in revolt.

"P-please," I stammered, my face burning, "I—I wish you wouldn't. . . . I'm engaged to a Tri Kappa at Goucher—"

"Just one kiss," she pleaded, her breath hot against my neck. In desperation I granted her boon, knowing full well that my weak defences were crumbling before the onslaught of this love tigree. Finally she allowed me to leave, but only after I had promised to dine at her pent-house apartment and have an intimate chat about the script. The basket of slave bracelets and marzipan I found awaiting me on my return home made me realize to what lengths Diana would go.

I was radiant that night in blue velvet tails and a bou-tonniere of diamonds from Cartier's, my eyes starry and the merest hint of cologne at my ear-lobes. An inscrutable Oriental served the Lucullan repast and my vis-à-vis was as effervescent as the wine.

"Have a bit of the wine, darling?" queried Diana solici-tously, indicating the roast Long Island airplane with applesauce. I tried to turn our conversation from the personal note, but Diana would have none of it. Soon we were exchanging gay bantam over the mellow Vouvray, laughing as we dipped fastidious fingers into the Crisco parfait for which Diana was famous. Our meal finished, we sauntered into the rumpus room and Diana turned on the radio. With a savage snarl the radio turned on her and we slid over the waxed floor in the intricate maze of the jackdaw strut. Without quite knowing why, I found myself hesitating before the plate of liqueur candies Diana was pressing on me.

"I don't think I should—really, I'm a trifle faint—"

"Oh, come on," she urged masterfully. "After all, you're old enough to be your father—I mean I'm old enough to be my mother. . . ." She stuffed a brandy bonbon between my clenched teeth. Before long I was eating them thirstily, reeling about the room and shouting snatches of coarse drunken doggerel. My brain was on fire, I tell you. Through the haze I saw Diana ffrench-Mamoulian, her nostrils dilated, groping for me. My scream of terror only egged her on, overturning chairs and tables in her bestial pursuit. With superhuman talons she tore off my collar and suspenders. I sank to my knees, choked with sobs, hanging on to my last shirt-stud like a drowning man. Her Svengali eyes were slowly hypnotizing me; I fought like a wounded bird—and then, blissful unconsciousness.

When I came to, the Oriental servant and Diana were battling in the center of the floor. As I watched, Yen Shee Gow drove a well-aimed blow to her mid-section, following it with a right cross to the jaw. Diana staggered and rolled under a table. Before my astonished eyes John Chinaman stripped the mask from his face and revealed the features of Blanche Almonds, a little seamstress I had long wooed unsuccessfully in New York. Gently she bathed my temples with Florida water and explained how she had followed me, suspecting Diana ffrench-Mamoulian's intentions. I let her rain kisses over my face and lay back in her arms as beaming Ivan tucked us in and cracked his whip over the prancing bays. In a few seconds our sleigh was skimming over the hard crust toward Port Arthur and freedom, leaving Plushnick's discomfited officers gnashing one another's teeth. The wintry Siberian moon glowed over the tundras, drenching my hair with moonbeams for Blanche to kiss away. And so, across the silvery steppes amid the howling of wolves, we rode into a new destiny, purified in the crucible that men call Hollywood.

P-S-S-T, PARTNER, YOUR
PERISTALSIS IS SHOWING

I was strolling aimlessly down Fifth Avenue the other afternoon when several dollars which had been burning a hole in my pocket suddenly burst into flame and I found myself in Brentano's. By the time my pants had stopped smoldering I discovered I owned a profusely illustrated set of Brantôme's spicy "Lives of Fair and Gallant Ladies," a brass paper knife, and a weird pamphlet called "Tobacco, the Weed That Made America Famous," by H. C. Apgar, of Elizabeth, New Jersey. The Brantôme I expect to dispose of at a profit; it just happens I know a high-school boy who is majoring in eighteenth-century court life. As for the paper knife, I may have a use for that also. One of these evenings, preferably a dark, overcast one, I am going out to Elizabeth, New Jersey, press it against somebody's gullet, and recover the dollar I paid for his pamphlet.

As I reconstruct it from the preface, Apgar broke with all stimulants, but particularly tobacco, some eighteen years ago, and since then has devoted his energy, of which he seems to have a frightening amount, to inducing the nation to follow his example. The response has been less than overwhelming, to judge from the annual income of George Washington Hill, but Apgar has gone on doggedly issuing jeremiads against the weed and such minor stimulants as chocolate, soda pop, and chewing gum, all of which he regards as pernicious in varying degrees. He exemplifies the sinister effect of chewing gum, for instance, with the case of "a woman troubled with a nervous twitching of the eyes, frightened at trivial noises, etc. Her trouble was diagnosed as Neurosis. She discontinued the use of gum and in six months her trouble was gone." An amazing cure, certainly, and one the American Psychiatric Association will do well to ponder at its next caucus. If Apgar's gloomy prognosis is correct, I fully expect to wind up in a ragged shawl outside the corner candy store, tearfully imploring my twitching, over-stimulated young to come home with me. Unfortunately, the author vitiates the force of his crusade somewhat by lapsing mysteriously into a long, wrangling denunciation of the Julian calendar. I lost the thread and assumed he was referring to the Julian Callender I used to know in Providence, a willowy party who ran a tearoom named the Lighted Taper and owned a first edition of "Jurgen." Luckily, I discovered my error just as I was sitting down to compose a pretty heated answer to what I consider an unprovoked assault.

Though Apgar's philippic differs little from the usual tract on the subject, it contains one feature of interest to students of the theatre, to say nothing of anybody possessing a full complement of vital organs. This is a purportedly comic dialogue between the brain and the stomach, intended to dramatize the penalty of indiscriminate eating and smoking. Like the true tyro, Apgar gives no stage direction to indicate where the colloquy is taking place, but I assume his players are standing before a painted drop, with a fountain in the background and rows of store fronts receding into the distance. There is probably a sidewalk clock on a standard marked "J. Weintraub, Jeweler—Home of Friendly Credit," the legend "Acme Lunch, Open All Night" on one of the shop windows, and a card on an easel reading "Brian BRAIN & Solly STOMACH—Society's Favorite Funsters." And, since Apgar is too preoccupied with moral fervor to characterize his action, we shall have to imagine for ourselves what they look like. The brain, I presume, is a fastidiously dressed straight man on the order of Eugene Howard, in a double-breasted jacket and straw hat, sporting a Malacca cane. The stomach, by contrast, wears a paper dickey, pants easily five sizes too large for him, a red putty nose, and huge, floppy shoes. Undoubtedly both carry bladders, or at least tambourines, with which they strike each other at intervals.

From its very first lines the skit betrays the poverty of invention and shallow understanding of his puppets typical of a reformer turned playwright:

BRAIN: Now, you listen to me, Stomach. That last mess of nourishment you sent up had nothing in it a dog could use.
STOMACH: Well, how could I help it? I did the best I could with the mess that was given me to digest, for your benefit.

How Apgar hoped to intrigue his audience with so pedestrian and maladroit an opening baffles comprehension. There are any number of provocative gambits he might have chosen. Brain and Stomach might hurry in from opposite wings, collide in center-stage, and embark on a noisy, good-humored argument in the manner of Quirt and Flagg. Or they could be fishing for pennies through a sidewalk grating when the shapely ankles of a saucy *midinette* (played by Heart) twinkle by. Or Brain can even fleece Stomach with a wallet stuffed with newspaper, whereupon the two of them join forces to swindle Liver, a humorous countryman with whiskers and portmanteau. The possibilities are infinite, but Apgar, bent double under a messianic complex, is hurrying to pile up his indictment. You can almost see Brain's smirk as he speaks his next line:

BRAIN: This man blames it all on you. He says you are always asking for more material to digest and he cannot resist the temptation to send it down to you. . . . This fellow is always complaining about his success in life. . . . Why, this poor sap has more alibis for his failures than the fellow who invented the word.

Here are a couple of distinguished protagonists indeed —two snarling, disgruntled loafers who have nothing better to do than lean on their shovels and criticize their employer. The taunt "This man blames it all on you" is especially diabolic. Brain, with a perverse spitefulness rivaling that of Bette Davis in her most poisonous rôles, is clearly trying to cause a rift between Stomach and the boss, and succeeding famously, as witness Stomach's reply:

STOMACH: You thought that last load of nourishment was bad, but wait until you get this one I am wrestling with now. Somebody invited him out tonight to play cards. They had a midnight "lunch" consisting of shrimp salad, mince pie covered with a thick creamy sauce, topped off with coffee strong enough to float an egg—I believe they call this demi-tasse; just a small cup of coffee to you and me. . . .

BRAIN: I thought something unusual was happening. I just received the effects of some beer, highballs, plenty of cigarettes, but no chewing tobacco. I wonder why he doesn't chew tobacco?

Notice, if you please, how cunningly this precious pair has created a portrait of the master as a slack-jawed imbecile, snob, and glutton. With consummate carelessness, Stomach observes that he attended a card game, a fact Brain seems to be unaware of. The assumption, consequently, is that this citizen leaves his brain at home when he gambles—scarcely a type of appeal to the popular mind. The sneering reference to "demi-tasse" implies further that he is fast becoming too big for his breeches and that homespun folks like Brain and Stomach refuse to be over-awed by such Gallicisms. If anything, though, Brain is the greater blackguard of the two, for his sniggering "I wonder why he doesn't chew tobacco?" reveals him not only as a sneak but a *provocateur*. He knows that a man in a weakened condition, coping with a hangover and a belly-ache, is open to any suggestion, no matter how desperate, but, like Samson, Brain is ready to pull down the whole human temple around him just for a laugh. Contemporary literature may yield up a more fiendish example of the will to self-destruction, but I doubt it.

Had Apgar motivated the action so that it built to a climax in which the man discovered this perfidy, excoriated his worthless apprentices, and flung them out into the night, he might have had an exciting, fast-moving melodrama. Or, employing honest emotional values, he could have constructed a situation whereby Brain and Stomach, in a moving renunciation scene out of Tolstoy, left to expiate their sins in the salt mines of Siberia. Instead, he permits his creatures to continue hurling cheap gibes at the man who pays for their bread and butter and closes on a note of defeatism and sabotage you would expect of such fifth columnists:

STOMACH: O.K., I'll take this matter up with him by producing an awful pain or sickness, as I know of no other way of appealing to him, but this won't do much good as he will drink some "likker" or send down some pills which are sure to be his old favorites—physic or aspirin.

BRAIN: O.K., Pal. Goodnight. See you in the morning with a headache.

If Apgar plans to trade on the current revival of interest in vaudeville and divert a few dollars into his pocket with this shoddy morality, he is reckoning without the public. Theatregoers will never disgorge two-twenty to be told their innards are spies, diversionists, and wreckers. Let him scrap his absurd mixture of soapy evangelism and tawdry cynicism; let him turn his hand to a gay, tuneful operetta based on fun in the ductless glands or depicting the viscera as jolly good fellows. And while he's at it, let him enclose that long-overdue dollar to his friend and well-wisher, S. J. Perelman.

A POX ON YOU,
MINE GOODLY HOST

A few nights ago I strolled into our Pompeian living room in my stocking feet, bedad, with a cigar in my mouth and a silk hat tilted back on my head, to find Maggie, with osprey plumes in her hair and a new evening cape, pulling on long white gloves. A little cluster of exclamation points and planets formed over her head as she saw me.

"Aren't you dressed yet, you bonehead?" she thundered. "Or were you sneaking down to Dinty Moore's for corned beef and cabbage with those worthless cronies of yours?" I soon banished the good woman's fears, and in response to my queries she drew from her reticule an advertisement clipped from the Sun. It displayed photographs of George S. Kaufman and Moss Hart framed in a family album over the legend "From Schrafft's Album of Distinguished Guests. The parade of luminaries who enjoy Schrafft's hearty dinners includes columnists, sportswriters, stage and radio personalities, football coaches, illustrators, producers. Adding to the glitter of this list are the distinguished names of Kaufman and Hart, who have written many a Broadway hit." Of course, nothing would do but we must dine at Schrafft's that very evening and mingle in the pageantry, so without further ado we set out.

Although it was not yet seven o'clock when our cab pulled up in front of the Forty-third Street branch, a sizable crowd of autograph-seekers had assembled and were eagerly scrutinizing each new arrival. A rapturous shout went up as I descended. "Here comes dashing Brian Aherne!" exulted a charming miss rushing forward. "Isn't it sickening?" I murmured into my wife's ear. "This happens everywhere—in stores, on buses—" "Yes, I know," she grated. "Everybody takes me for Olivia de Havilland. Get out of the way, you donkey. Don't you see the man's trying to get by?" To my surprise, I found myself brushed aside by Brian Aherne, who must have been clinging to the trunk rack. As I shouldered my way after him, curious stares followed me. "That must be his bodyguard," commented a fan. "That shrimp couldn't be a cat's bodyguard," sneered his neighbor. I looked the speaker full in the eye. "That's for the cat to say," I riposted, and as the bystanders roared, I stalked through the revolving doors, conscious I had scored.

Buoyant the advertisement had been, but I was frankly dazzled by the scene which confronted me. The foyer, ablaze with lights, was peopled by personages of such distinction as few first nights attract. Diamonds of the finest water gleamed at the throats of women whose beauty put the gems to shame, and if each was not escorted by a veritable Adonis, he was at least a Greek. A hum of well-bred conversation rose from the throng, punctuated now and again by the click of expensive dentures. In one corner Nick Kenny, Jack Benny, James Rennie, Sonja Henie, and E. R. Penney, the chain-store magnate, were gaily comparing pocketbooks to see who had the most money, and in another Jim Thorpe chatted with Jay Thorpe, cheek by jowl with Walter Wanger and Percy Grainger. Here Lou Little and Elmer Layden demonstrated a new shift to a fascinated circle, while there Ann Corio demonstrated still another to an even more spellbound circle. Myron Selznick, Frank Orsatti, and Leland Hayward had just planed in from the Coast to sign everyone to agency contracts, and now, swept along by sheer momentum, were busily signing each other. As far as the eye could see, at tables in the background, gourmets were gorging themselves on chicken-giblet-and-cream-cheese sandwiches, apple pandowdy, and orange snow. One fine old epicure, who had ordered a sizzling platter without specifying what food was to be on it, was nevertheless eating the platter itself and smacking his lips noisily. Small wonder that several world-famed illustrators, among them Henry Raleigh, Norman Rockwell and Pruett Carter, had set up easels and were limning the brilliant scene with swift strokes. I was drinking in every detail of the shifting panorama when a hostess well over nine feet tall, with ice mantling her summit, waved me toward a door marked "Credentials."

"We—we just wanted the old-fashioned nut pudding with ice-cream sauce, Ma'am," I stammered.

"That's up to the committee, Moozeer," she said briskly. "If we let in every Tom, Dick and Harry who wanted the old-fashioned nut pudding with ice-cream sauce . . . Ah, good evening, Contessa! Back from Hobe Sound already?"

I entered a small room exquisitely furnished in Biedermeier and took my place in a short queue of applicants. Most of them were obviously under tension, and the poor wretch in front of me was a pitiable spectacle. His eyes rolled wildly, tremors shook his frame, and it was apparent he entertained small hope of meeting the rigorous requirements.

"What have Kaufman and Hart got that I haven't got?" he demanded of me desperately. "I bought a house in Bucks County and wrote two plays, both smash hits, even if they didn't come to New York. Why, you ought to see the reviews *Tea and Strumpets* and *Once in a Wifetime* got in Syracuse!" I reassured him as best I could, but his premonitions were well founded, for a few moments later he was ignominiously dispatched to dine at a cafeteria. I was shuffling forward to confront the tight-lipped examiners when a scuffle broke out in the foyer and Kaufman and Hart, bundled in astrakhan greatcoats and their eyes flashing fire, were herded in unceremoniously.

"What is the meaning of this—this bestiality?" sputtered Hart. "How dare you bar us from this bourgeois *bistro*?"

"I've been thrown out of better restaurants than this!" boomed Kaufman, rapidly naming several high-class restaurants from which he had been ejected. The chairman of the board picked up a dossier and turned a cold smile on the playwrights.

"Naturally, we regret any inconvenience to you gentlemen," he said smoothly, "but our house rules are inflexible. You wrote a play called *Lady in the Dark*, did you not, Mr. Hart?" Hart regarded him stonily. "Starring Gertrude Lawrence, I believe?"

"Yes," snapped Hart, "and she's sitting right up at the

fountain this minute having a rum-and-butter-toffee sundae with chopped pecans."

"Why were we not shown the script of that play, Mr. Hart?" The chairman's voice was silky with menace. "Why was nobody in the Frank G. Shattuck organization consulted regarding casting?"

"I—I meant to," quavered Hart. "I swear I did! I told my secretary—I made a note—"

"Thought you'd smuggle it into town without us, did you?" snarled the chairman. "Let 'em read the out-of-town notices in *Variety*, eh?" A tide of crimson welled up the alabaster column of Hart's neck, and he stood downcast, staring at his toecaps. Kaufman would fain have interceded for his associate, but the chairman stopped him with a curt gesture.

"Hamburg Heaven for thirty days," he barked. "Take 'em away."

"Help, help!" screamed the luckless duo, abasing themselves. But no vestige of pity lurked in the chairman's granite visage, and an instant later they were borne, kicking and squealing, from the chamber by two brawny attendants.

And now little else remains to be told. How I managed to elude my captors and steal the superb mocha cupcake the natives call "The Star of Forty-third Street Between Sixth Avenue and Broadway" must be left to another chronicle. Suffice to say that whenever your mother and I pass Schrafft's, she turns to me with a secret smile and we continue right on up to Lindy's. We can still get in there without a visa.

SLOW — DANGEROUS FOIBLES AHEAD!

Some years ago, about the time Clayton, Jackson, and Durante were twisting you around their little finger at the Parody Club, there was a strange and shabby clip joint around the corner on West Forty-ninth Street. The patrons of this rookery were chiefly small, tight men who were understood to be on the lam, and a few Fordham undergraduates affecting an insolence found only at New Haven. The floor show consisted of a couple of refugees from the Orpheum circuit exchanging breezy cross-fire and flailing each other into insensibility. There was nothing at all exceptional about these two artists, but every now and again, on alternate Tuesdays, the straight man would pause in his routine and with studied ambiguity deliver a remark to his partner which mysteriously electrified a number of the customers. The expression ran, "The stuff is here—and it's mellow." Eventually one of the illuminati, whose name oddly enough happened to be Tony Illuminati, took pity on my bewilderment. He explained that a fresh shipment of happy dust had just arrived and might be purchased from the cigarette girl.

Well, the stuff is here again—and mellow it is indeed. The editors of Vogue, ever quick to sniff out the trend and interpret the mode, recently called in nine important American industrial designers and asked them each to create a dress for the Woman of the Future in the World of Tomorrow. The boys spat on their hands—their own hands, not those of the editors of Vogue—and leapt to

103

their T-squares. The results were run up by nine leading New York shops, photographed by nine leading photographers named Anton Bruehl, and appear on nine pages of the February issue. And in case you think there's nothing to numerology, Mummy has had a simply blinding headache for the past nine days.

After a hasty peek into their crystal ball, the designers were unanimous in the opinion that the Girl of Tomorrow would differ considerably from Miss 1943, who, it appears, is little better than a bundle of assorted neuroses, bronchitis, and stocking runs. "Medical Science will have made her body Perfect," fluently reports Mr. Donald Deskey. "She'll never know obesity, emaciation, colds in the head, superfluous hair, or a bad complexion—thanks to a controlled diet, controlled basal metabolism. Her height will be increased, her eyelashes lengthened—with some X-hormone." Lest this terrify you or remind you of Mr. Max Beerbohm's description of posterity in *Enoch Soames* (". . . all of them smelling rather strongly of carbolic. And all of them quite hairless"), Mr. George Sakier adds a reassuring note: "The woman of the future will be tall and slim and lovely; she will be bred to it—for the delectation of the community and her own happiness. She will have a new freedom in time and space. She will move in a world of vast horizons. Her viewpoint will be clear and direct. She will be free from complexes and inhibitions. Her clothes will be simple and free from fantasy. She will take the miracles of science for granted, and will not make a fetish of functional forms, or of design-for-function." I breathed a little easier when I read that,

104

Every time you ask your hostess at a party these days, "Who is that tall girl in the corner with the enchanting bosom?" you invariably get the careless reply, "Oh, that's Liane. She makes a fetish of functional forms and design-for-function." And as if this weren't bad enough, it always turns out Liane has a manic-depressive husband who makes a fetish of hitting people who tickle his wife.

Given this superb chassis, the designers seem evenly divided about upholstering it. Messrs. Teague, Sakier, Deskey, and Dreyfuss feel that the maximum of it will be put on display, and consequently package the Woman of Tomorrow in transparent chiffon, glass yarn, and cellophane; Mr. Dreyfuss, who, I take it, is a more old-fashioned type boy, favors a skin-tight black net, which was good enough for my grandfather and is good enough for me. "These materials," explains Mr. Teague of his fabrics of the future, "will be of chemical origin, and many will be either transparent or translucent, *with an individual life of their own.*" I hope this last phrase of Mr. Teague's is purely figurative; offhand, the thought of clothes leading an existence independent of their owner is a little on the spooky side. How are you going to remain cool and poised on that future day when you demand hotly of your wife, "Where in the hell are those pants I threw over that chair last night?" only to get the answer, "Oh, they went up to Pride's Crossing for the weekend with my girdle. They'll be back Tuesday morning"?

The other camp among the designers—Messrs. Wright, Loewy, Arens, and Platt—is much more inclined to stress woman's age-old desire for fancy plumage. To this end they wrap her in aluminum foil, woollens interwoven with electric wire, and as yet undiscovered fabrics, to quote Mr. Loewy, "of microscopic cellular construction, made of a contracting and expanding fibre." What is this awful preoccupation with having your clothes twitch around in a horrid little life of their own? Did I miss something? I have the strange feeling that I have been asleep for twenty years and that everybody is jeering at my unkempt hair and rusty fowling piece.

When it comes to Milady's accessories, there is no holding back the boys; they just lay back on the hip and puff till the bunk is blue with smoke. "She may wear in her hair a headlight," says Mr. Wright of his model in evening dress, "an ornamental cylinder with a huge man-made diamond electrically lighted." The least her escort could do under the circumstances is carry an old-fashioned stem-winding watch and whistle at the grade crossings. Mr. Arens, dressing a hypothetical bride in glass, confines her waist in a sequin belt, of which he says, "These sequins are really 'Stimsonite' traffic reflectors of Lucite, made by the Signal Service Corporation. They are warranted to pick up and reflect the light from an automobile headlight a mile distant," which certainly ought to prove a boon to the innumerable brides who are members of the United States Army Signal Corps. Mr. Dreyfuss provides his miss with a combination electric fan and vanity case, described as follows: "Nothing coquettish about it, for it will get its current by radio waves through the ether and will cool this girl, as well as clip the noses of any unwelcome suitors. The propeller-like blades, made of a transparent plastic, will fold into the interior, which is commodious enough to carry the eight million contraptions that crowd today's purses. (It was executed by Volupté.)" I trust I do not speak with bitterness, Mr. Dreyfuss, but to clothe a young lady in skin-tight black net and then hand her a gadget for clipping unwelcome suitors' noses is no way to creep into my heart. It may be Volupté to you, but it's only loose thinking to me.

Of the nine designers, only one, Mr. Gilbert Rohde, thinks women's clothes good enough as they are, but he believes men's clothes need radical revision. Mr. Rohde envisions the man of the twenty-first century in a ski suit knitted of a mixture of transparent synthetic yarn and infinitely fine beryllium threads, whose color can be changed by varying the plating of the beryllium copper wire. "The gentleman, for example, may start to the office in a rich gun-metal Solo-suit, drab in color, but scintillating with life. [There's that same dreadful insistence on the material's moiling and churning.] In the afternoon, there is a directors' meeting, so he changes to a deep maroon; and for dinner, the change is made in a jiffy to turquoise." On this man's head Mr. Rohde places an "Antenna Hat," rather similar in design to the coils of a copper still: "It snatches radio and Omega waves out of the ether—here, at last, is man's opportunity to escape from the deadly monotony of the twentieth-century male hat." The delightful prospect of having Guy Lombardo playing about your head and ears is enough to stir the pulse of the most apathetic. Mr. Man of Tomorrow will further wear a modish surtout called the Plastivest, fashioned of

Plexiglas—two words, incidentally, which I will thank Mr. Rohde to tow out to sea and burn at his earliest convenience. This appalling little vest is designed to contain a two-way telephone, radio set, office equipment, and control switches for the air waves which heat and cool the suit. The feet, presumably with streamlined bunions, are to be encased in nothing more or less than congress gaiters "with breather pores just large enough for air, but too small for water"; and, finally, men will have returned to wearing long hair and marcelled beards in the fashion of Artaxerxes. "And perhaps we shall find a few platinum blondes, too," murmurs Mr. Rohde engagingly.

For two days now I have been crouching in a corner of this coal bin, enjoying a peace I never thought possible. Of course, the grit gets in your teeth and there's a leak in that pipe overhead, but on the other hand it's just a trifle too dark for reading. Why, you couldn't even see your hand before your face, particularly if it were holding a copy of Vogue. And goodness knows, it'll be a long time before it's steady enough for *that*.

FOOTNOTE ON THE YELLOW PERIL

If you have been bothered with any mysterious aches or pains this summer, Bellevue Hospital has been going around the last few days cockily puffing out its chest because it has acquired a new laboratory of tropical medicine. Just drop down there and they will be glad to tell you at a glance whether you are suffering from sprue, the Delhi boil, Madura foot, Bilharzia and related fluke diseases (Bilharzia is no fluke, let me tell you; there's nobody to blame but yourself), the Peruvian wart, or any of the various forms of pork trichinae. I am even thinking of going down there myself for a little reupholstering. Mine isn't exactly a physical thing, unless I caught something from reading Alice Tisdale Hobart's books; it's more of a Far Eastern mental complaint. I just can't seem to tell those Chinese war lords apart.

The trouble started a long time ago when Chiang, the Premier of China (have I made any mistakes so far?), went over to borrow a cup of opium from Chang and exchange gossip. Now, that shouldn't be hard: Chiang went to chin with Chang. This Chang is "Young" Chang and should not be confused with "Old" Chang, his father, the one-time ruler of Manchuria. As soon as I found this out, I started confusing them, and it didn't help any to learn that "Young" Chang has two brothers of the same name. One of them is this harum-scarum younger brother whom the Chinese simply adore and call "that murtherin' shpalpeen, wurra wurra." The other is a Communist and lives in Moscow; his people distinguish him from his brother as "Faith, that murtherin' Rooshian bhoyo."

Just when I had all this neatly pegged and was going along leading a life of Buddhistic calm, contemplating my navel, Chang decided to kidnap Chiang. What his motive was I can't imagine, unless it was to confuse me horribly. The paper I read it in unfortunately happened to carry as well a publicity release about a new book called "Yang and Yin." At the close of business that day, the old prickly sensation had returned and I found myself bursting into tears over the most trivial matters. I spent a white night trying to straighten myself out, but by morning all I managed to remember was that I had once seen a film called "Chang" with a very cute monkey in it. I had barely pinned on my pigtail and sat down to my breakfast of steamed rice and bamboo shoots when a woman representing herself as my wife lifted her head from a theatrical magazine and asked me if I had ever seen Della Fox in "Wang."

I slid out of my chair barking like a Pekingese and mercifully fainted away.

It was touch and go with me for forty-eight hours, and I'd like to take this opportunity of thanking my wife and the three concubines for their unsparing devotion in my behalf. Soon, however, the crisis was past, and then came long, slow days of convalescence, with my collie bounding beside me on the lawn and tugging at my parasol. Good old Towser! I'd like to take this opportunity of thanking him for his unsparing devotion. For it was on Towser that the burden fell of dressing the children, undressing the concubines, and eating my gruel, without which I would have recovered in half the time.

As soon as my Number One boy spread word through the concession that the foreign devil was well again, the Chinese sprang to attention. "Young" Chang ("Old" Chang's son, but not "Scalawag" Chang or "Red" Chang) offered to return the Generalissimo (you'd better hold onto the rails; I'm beginning to pitch slightly) to Soong, who didn't give a hang but was only negotiating for his sister (who is married to Chiang). At this point two more generals, who had been waiting in the wings until they heard my pulses begin to hammer, entered the scene. Their names might just as easily have been Rosencrantz and Guildenstern, but no; they had to be named Yang and Feng. Yang was a Chinese version of General Jubal A. Early who hoped to highjack the whole enterprise; Feng, who is called "the Christian Marshal" (as opposed to Feng, the Jewish Marshal, I guess), had no real business there, but claimed the conductor had given him a wrong transfer. Chang—no, Yang—told Chiang—wait a minute, Chiang told Yang that Feng, who is Soong . . .

From now on everything is quicksand, and if it's all right with you, I'll just sit here under this banyan tree and read a nice, quiet book. I'm almost halfway through Jack London's *White Fang*, but it isn't holding me. I may slip around the corner to the movies—they have a very interesting picture there, I understand. It's called *The General Died at Dawn*, about a Chinese war lord named Yang. The only trouble is that Clifford Odets, who wrote it, is keeping company with one Luise Rainer, and she plays the lead in *The Good Earth*, which is about a character named Wang. And now they tell me Mr. Odets is going to do a story for a producer named Wanger. *For goodness' sake, has everybody gone stark, staring Wang?*

MIDWINTER
FACIAL TRENDS

A scenario writer I know, who had been working uninterruptedly in Hollywood for three years, finally got back to New York for a two-week vacation. He had barely unpacked his gold-backed military hairbrushes and put on a red moiré smoking jacket when a wire from his agent ordered him back to the Coast for an assignment. The young man preferred to stay, but his conscience reminded him of the two hundred and fifty thousand dollars in annuities he was carrying, and this in turn summoned up a frightening picture of a destitute old age when he might have to work on a newspaper again and ride in streetcars. After wrestling with himself for several hours, he decided to assert his independence. He sent back a spunky wire to the effect that he was working on a novel and could not return under any conditions unless his salary was raised to seventeen hundred and fifty dollars a week, instead of fifteen hundred. Then he forgot all about it, except to lie awake three nights and stay indoors waiting for the telephone to ring.

To nobody's surprise, the deal went through, and forty-eight hours later the scenario writer was sitting in a producer's office in Hollywood, a little worse for the plane trip and a box of sodium Amytal tablets. In a few badly chosen words the producer explained his predicament. He had a terrific story; it smelled box office a mile away. But every writer on the payroll had been stumped for the last three months by one detail.

113

"I'll tell you the meat of the story," said the producer. "It's got plenty of spontinuity when you maul it over in your mind, only just this one little thing you got to figure out."

"Give," murmured the scenario writer, closing his eyes to indicate that his faculties were purring like a Diesel engine.

"We fade in on a street in London," began the producer, fading in on a street in London. "It's about four o'clock in the morning and I see a guy dressed in rags dragging himself along through the fog, a Lon Chaney type guy. He's all twisted and crippled up. Voom! All of a sudden he ducks down an areaway and knocks on a door. It opens and I see a gorgeous hallway with Chinese rugs and Ming vases. We hold the camera on it and milk whatever we can from the scene. The minute the guy's inside, he straightens up, takes off this harness, and unties his leg. What I mean is, the guy's as normal as you or me. Any audience'll buy that—am I right? Then we truck with him through a door and he's in like a hospital corridor. He pulls on rubber gloves and an operating gown—"

"Wait a minute," the writer interrupted, rising. "Am I supposed to spot laughs in this?"

"Siddown," commanded the producer. "There's a million opportunities for good crazy dialogue later on. We wipe the guy into an operating room and pan around. He's got ten, fifteen beautiful dames chained to the walls with practically nothing on, and if that don't kill 'em, I don't know show business. The legal department's taking it up with the Hays office this afternoon. We follow the guy over to a bench that's full of test tubes and scientific stuff; he pours one test tube into another and hollers, 'I got it! The life secret I been hunting for years!' Mind you, this ain't dialogue—I'm just spitballing. So then he puts a little of this life secret in a hypodermic needle and rings a gong. These two assistants wheel in a table with our leading woman on it, out like a light. Our guy rubs his hands and laughs like a hyena. He picks up the hypo, bends over our girl, and that's where you got to figure out this one thing."

"What's that?" the writer inquired suspiciously. The producer bit the end off a manufacturer's size Corona, frustration in his eyes, and shook his head.

"What kind of a business is this guy in?" he asked help-lessly.

If you are inclined to brood easily, I can guarantee that this question will tease you to the brink of hysteria. It obsessed me almost constantly until I stumbled across what may very well be the answer. It is contained in a little 134-page brochure entitled Cosmetic Surgery, by Charles C. Miller, M.D., published by the author in 1907. Since that day several weeks ago when I first peeped into this attractive volume, bound in red sharkskin, I have been confined to my rooms in the Albany with a fairly constant attack of the rams. As if Dr. Miller's prose style were not sufficiently graphic, the text is supplemented with half a dozen photographs and a score of drawings calculated to make your scalp tingle. I am no sissy, but I will risk a sporting flutter of half a guinea that even the brothers Mayo would have flinched under *Cosmetic Surgery.*

The author starts off casually enough with instructions for correcting outstanding ears, which range all the way from tying them flat to the head to some pretty violent surgery. Personally, I have found that a short length of three-quarter-inch Manila hemp bound stoutly about the head, the knot protruding below one's felt hat, adds a rakish twist to the features and effectively prisons ears inclined to flap in the wind. A salty dash may be imparted to the ensemble by dipping the rope in tar, or even substituting oakum for hemp.

I must confess that the chapter headed "Nose with the Bulbous Tip," on page 50, fired my blood, and I read three or four pages avidly waiting for the appearance of Hercule Poirot or even Inspector Lestrade before I discovered that no crime had been committed. But on page 79, just as I finished yawning through some hints on diminishing the unduly large mouth by hemstitching it at the corners, Dr. Miller plucked the roses from my cheeks with "Marginal Tattooing as a Means of Adding to the Apparent Width of the Lips." That may not be your idea of a punchy title for the marquee of a theatre, but if Boris Karloff were in it, you'd pay your six-sixty fast enough. Living as I do on the hem of the wilderness, I was not aware that "tattooing about the margin of the lips to overcome undue thinness" had become a commonplace. The technique is as follows: "The skin is punctured or pricked open with a needle. The puncturing does not extend through the skin, but merely into the true skin.

116

[Come, come, Doctor, let's not quibble.] After the punc tures have been made, the coloring is rubbed in with the point of the needle or with a slightly flattened spud. Some reaction may be expected to follow the operation, but healing is complete in a few days." Why any reaction save boredom should follow rubbing a patient's lips with a potato is not clear to me, but I suppose that if one were allergic to potatoes, one might become restless under the massage. Speaking for myself, I have always been very partial to potatoes, especially those of the cottage-fried type.

It is on page 92, with "The Formation of the Dimple," that Dr. Miller really removes the buttons from the foils. "It is my practice in these cases," he states, "to thoroughly scrub the cheek, and then, after having the patient smile, select the point where a dimple should form under ordi- nary circumstances. . . . I mark this point, and insert my hypodermic needle." The operative method from now on is strikingly similar to fishing for perch through a hole in the ice. The Doctor lowers a line with a bobber and a bit of red flannel, builds a fire on the patient's forehead, and sits down to warm his hands till a dimple is hooked. The patient lies there softly whimpering, "I didn't have enough trouble, I had to have dimples like Robert Taylor yet!" And there let us leave them in the softly flickering firelight, with the thought that it will flicker much better if you pile on an occasional page out of Cosmetic Surgery, by Charles C. Miller.

COUNTER-REVOLUTION

The other night a forty-five-year-old friend of mine, after ingesting equal portions of Greek fire and artillery punch, set out to prove that he could walk across a parquet flooring on his hands while balancing a vase on his head. As a consequence, about eleven o'clock the following morning he was being trepanned at the Harkness Pavilion and I was purchasing a bottle of Major's Cement. I had reassembled the shards and was about to uncork the cement bottle when the bold yellow leaflet in which it was wrapped caught my eye. To predict that this small circular will eventually outrank Magna Carta and the Peace of Breda in historical significance may seem audacious. Yet even the most frivolous cannot escape its implications, for in a single decisive stroke it alters the entire status of the consumer.

From its opening sentence, the document was marked by a note of brooding, reminiscent of a manifesto:

If we could make the cement in liquid form and transparent, and at the same time as strong and as proof against moisture as it is now, we would be glad to do so. But this cannot be done.

A dozen lines further on, the manufacturer was fretting again over the possible imputation that he was holding back on his product:

If we could make a cement transparent and in liquid form as strong as the way we make our cement, we would do it.

There is no material that you could use that would make cement that way.

Obviously an *idée fixe*, I thought to myself, but aloud, I merely said quietly, "All right now, I can hear you. I use Leonard's Ear Oil as well as Major's Cement." My witty reprimand fell among thorns; a moment later the circular was behaving like a regular ogre:

If you do not succeed the first time in mending an article, do not throw up your hands and go pulling your hair and yell out "I have been swindled once more"; but have patience, for the Cement is all right.

By now I was thoroughly nettled. Patience, eh? Look who's telling me to have patience. Why, I've got more patience in my little fing—but my words were blotted out in a last echoing apoplectic bellow:

If, before doing as suggested, you tell others that the Cement is no good, you are saying an untruth and injuring the reputation of Major's Cement. Remember the Golden Rule, "Do unto others as you would be done by."

Since I long ago gave instructions to strew my ashes to the four winds when the hour sounds, this precept left me with only one course open, and I took it.

It is obvious that such a *volte-face* in sales technique is fraught with the most far-reaching implications. There is every chance that Major's plaintive exasperation with the customer may yet be adopted and distorted by other firms. I take the liberty of presenting a few glamorous possibilities in a curtain-raiser, with the hope that it may inspire some fellow-dramatist to attempt a more sustained flight:

(Scene: The men's furnishing section of a large department store. As the curtain rises, a salesman, Axel Munthe, is waiting on a patron. Munthe is not related to the physician who wrote "The Story of San Michele"; it is simply an interesting coincidence. Enter Leonard DeVilbiss, a typical customer—in fact, a luggage tag reading "Mr. Average Consumer" depends from the skirt of his topcoat. He looks timidly at Munthe.)

DeVilbiss—Do you sell Mackinaws here?

Munthe—No, we give 'em away. That's how we stay in business—giving away free Mackinaws.

DeVilbiss—I don't see any around here.

Munthe—What the devil do you think those are hanging on the rack—flounders?
(DeVilbiss meekly takes a seat and, picking up copies of "Click," "Pic," and "Look," begins to hold the pages against the light to discover possible salacious effects.)

Patron (uncertainly)—I don't know about these shorts. I had in mind something with a banjo seat.

Munthe—Banjo seat! Banjo seat! Why don't you wear a banjo and be done with it?

Patron—These won't shrink, will they?

Munthe—Look—Boulder Dam shrank six inches last year. You want me to underwrite a pair of lousy ninety-eight-cent shorts against it?

120

PATRON—Hmm. Well, I think I'll look around.

MUNTHE—Not in here, you won't. If you want to browse, go to a bookstore. (*Patron exits; Munthe approaches DeVilbiss*) All right, Buster, break it up. You're not in your club.

DEVILBISS—I'd like to try on some Mackinaws.

MUNTHE (*suspiciously*)—Got any money?

DEVILBISS—Yes, sir. (*He shows Munthe some money. Latter reluctantly pulls out rack.*)

MUNTHE—Now, let me see. You want something in imported camel's hair, fleece-lined, with a life-time guarantee, for only five dollars?

DEVILBISS (*dazzled*)—Sure.

MUNTHE—That's what I thought. They all do. Well, cookie, you're in the wrong pew.

DEVILBISS (*humbly*)—Haven't you any shoddy old blue plaid ones with leatheroid buttons for about fifty dollars?

MUNTHE—To fit a little shrimp like you?

DEVILBISS (*submissively*)—It don't have to fit me.

MUNTHE (*bridling*)—Oh, you're not going to wear it, hey? Just one of those sneaking comparison shoppers who—

DEVILBISS—No, no—I thought for carrying out the ashes—you know, around the cellar.

MUNTHE (*loftily*)—You must be a pretty small-time lug to carry out your own ashes.

DEVILBISS—I am.

MUNTHE (*grudgingly*)—Well, all right. Slip this on for size.

DeVilbiss (*after a struggle*)—It binds me a little under the arms.

Munthe—You're damn right it does. If we knew how to lick that, we'd all be in clover.

DeVilbiss—Could you—I mean, maybe if a seam was let out—that is, the sleeve—

Munthe (*infuriated*)—See here, chump, if you think I'm going to rebuild a measly fifty-dollar Mackinaw for every stumblebum who mooches in off the street—

DeVilbiss—Oh, no. I wouldn't dream of asking you! I—I was just wondering whether Alberta—that's Mrs. DeVilbiss; she's a regular whiz at things like that—and time, say, she's got all the time in the world—

Munthe—O.K., come on. Do you want it or don't you?

DeVilbiss—You bet your life I do! Does—er—does this model come with pockets?

Munthe—Yes, and we throw in two tickets to a musical and dinner at Voisin's. (*Shouting*) What the hell do you think we're running here, a raffle?

DeVilbiss—Gee, you got me wrong. I wouldn't want anything I wasn't entitled to, honest!

Munthe—Next thing I know you'll be chiseling me out of paper and string to carry it home.

DeVilbiss—My goodness, no! I'll put it right over my arm—it's no trouble, really!

Munthe (*taking money from DeVilbiss*)—Say, if I'd known you had nothing but twenties—

DeVilbiss—Gosh, never mind the change—that's quite all right. Thank you very much.

Munthe—Now, listen, chum, watch your step. If I hear

any squawk out of you about our merchandise, I'll cool you off fast enough.

(*DeVilbiss exits hurriedly. A moment later Lin Yutang, the floorwalker—also no relation to the author of "The Story of San Michele"—enters.*)

YUTANG (*glowering*)—Look here, Munthe, was that a customer I just saw coming out of this section?

MUNTHE (*quickly*)—Of course not, sir. It was only a shoplifter.

YUTANG—All right, then, but don't let me catch you selling anything around here. You know the policy of this store. Carry on!

(*Munthe returns his salute and, picking up a bottle of acid, begins to dump it over the goods as Yutang, arms folded, watches him approvingly.*)

CURTAIN

THE LOVE DECOY

A Story of Youth in College Today—Awake, Fearless, Unashamed

"Professor Gompers is ill!" The whisper spread like wildfire through the packed classroom. A feeling of emulsion swept over me. Kindly old Professor Gompers, whose grizzled chin and chiselled grin had made his name a byword at Tunafish College for Women! Ivy Nüdnick, sauciest co-ed in the class, she of the unruly locks and the candied gray eyes, leaned over to impart the latest gossip.

"That new instructor, Russell Gipf, is subbing for him!" The color drained slowly from my face, entered the auricle, shot up the escalator, and issued from the ladies' and misses' section into the housewares department. I remembered Russell Gipf as a lean brown giant in tweeds whose resemblance to Warren William had caused his suspension the year before. It had been an ugly scandal but luckily his nose was broken in an accident soon after and the faculty had restored him. Dreamily I recalled an autumn afternoon when I had visited him in his office in ivy-colored Schneider to discuss a theme I had written. Through the half-open windows drifted the mingled smell of wood smoke and freshmen. He confided that he was doing research in dirty limericks for his doctor's thesis and asked if I knew any "Good Ones." In the twinkling of an eye we were in the gutter. At no time, however, did he allow himself the usual indecent proposal, and I returned to my dormitory room raging, determined never to see him again.

An impatient voice summoned me rudely from my daydream. I looked up; Russell Gipf was addressing me crisply from the platform. My feminine eye noted that he was still a spiffy dresser, a regular up-to-the-minute gink.

"Will you please answer the question, Miss Hornbostel?"

"I—I didn't hear it," I quavered.

"Well, Miss 'Lame Brain'," he retorted sardonically, "maybe you had better stop galvanizing around nights and pay attention!" A cold fury welled up in me and I longed to hang one on his lug for his insolence. I was seething but he could not see it, for several of my girl chums were seething in front of me. A moment later the bell tolling in ivy-covered Hoffenstein brought the class to a close. Slipping my pencil box and pen wipers into my corsage I approached his desk, a plan fermenting in my brain.

"Yes, Miss Hornbostel?" Russell Gipf's eyes were dancing with fun.

"Oh, Mr. Gipf," I began, "I hardly know how to say this. It—it's so personal." His eyes stopped dancing with fun and began dancing with sex.

"Go on," he urged.

"I—I can't get the cap off my toothpaste," I faltered, a tear trembling on my nose. "If you could only help me . . ." I gazed out of my huge bedroom eyes appealingly.

"Well, now—ahem—this is serious," he said slowly. "No wonder you weren't prepared in class just now. Naturally, you were upset."

"And you were cruel," I said.

"I'm sorry," he added Quigley.

"Why did you add Quigley?" I begged him. He apologized and subtracted Quigley, then divided Hogan. We hastily dipped the slices of Hogan into Karo, poured sugar over them, and ate them with relish.

"Tell me," said Gipf, as he wiped his mouth on the tail of his shirt, "about this toothpaste: if you could bring the tube to my office . . ."

I explained hurriedly that it was too heavy to carry and that he would have to come up to my dormitory room that evening after "lights out." He readily fell in with my wish and promised. As we walked across the campus toward ivy-covered Lapidus, I drew him out craftily. He had been in the north of Scotland that summer shooting bob-tail flushes, and he was full of his subject. Although I hated him, I had to confess that his smile made my pulses sing, and I gladly would have leaped through a hoop had he asked me to. He must have been aware of it, for he suddenly reached into his green baize bag and produced a hoop.

"Here, leap through this hoop, you," he ordered. I did so and he flicked me lightly with his whip. I saw his face go dark with passion. "Dolores—I love you!" he whispered, his hand closing over mine. Mine in turn closed over his. In an instant we had chosen up sides, it was my turn at bats, and I knocked a sizzling bunt to Pipgrass in the daisies.

"Ah, cara mia, giz a kiz," panted Russell. I tried to resist his overtures, but he plied me with symphonies, quartets, chamber music and cantatas. I felt myself softening, but I was determined to go through with my plan.

"Are you mad, Russell?" I stopped him haughtily. He bit his lip in a manner which immediately awakened my maternal sympathy, and I helped him bite it. Foolish man! In a trice the animal in him rose to the surface again. He caught my arm in a vice-like grip and drew me to him, but with a blow I sent him groveling. In ten minutes he was back with a basket of appetizing fresh-picked grovels. We squeezed them and drank the piquant juice thirstily. Then I blew him an airy kiss.

"Tonight—at ten-thirty, *mon désir!*" I flung at him over my shoulder. Even in my room I could hear him panting four floors below on the campus as I changed to a filmy negligee and began to cold-cream my glowing cheeks.

The dim glow of shaded lamps and the heady intoxication of incense had transformed my room into a veritable Oriental bower when Russell Gipf knocked cautiously on my door at ten-thirty. From the ostermoor where I was stretched out lazily, I murmured an inviting "Come in!"

"Come in!" I murmured invitingly. He entered shaking himself vigorously. There had been a heavy fall of talcum several hours before and as far as the ground could see the eye was white. I offered Russell a dish of soap flakes, but despite my attempts to put him at his ease he seemed nervous.

"The—the toothpaste," he began, looking about suspiciously. I indicated the bathroom with a lazy finger. In a moment he reappeared, his face haggard and his eyes like burning holes in the snow.

"Yes," I shot at him coldly, "I tricked you. No, it's useless to try the door—and it's a four-story drop straight down from those windows, Mr. Russell Gipf. Perhaps you're wondering what I intend to do now." I picked up the telephone, my voice a snarl. "In five minutes the faculty will break in and find you in a co-ed's room. What will your wealthy old father Prosper Gipf, president of the Absconders' and Defaulters' National Bank, say to that?" He backed away from me whimpering piteously. But I was goading him on as only a raging woman can. "You humiliated me in front of all my classmates today. Now—you shall pay." My hand was lifting the receiver when a faint scratching sounded at the door, followed by stertorous breathing. I threw it open. Dean Fothergill, his face that of a man mad with desire, lunged at me.

"Dolores," he implored, "you adorable little witch— I've been following you with my eyes—I . . ."

"You rotter!" I turned in surprise at Russell Gipf's voice as he flashed past me and drove a decisive blow into the aged roué's kidneys. The two men grappled, their teeth bared. Russell's head snapped back as Dean Fothergill, who I forgot to say was once amateur light-heavyweight boxing champion of University of California at Los Angeles, drove a decisive blow to the Gipf kidneys. The noise of fist on kidneys rang out in the still air. I watched the spectacle unmoved. After all, tomorrow I would have to pass my law exam; I opened *Fist on Kidneys* and was deep in it when I heard a groan. I looked up. There, manacled to Russell Gipf, stood Dean Fothergill, a hangdog expression on his face.

"Well, Miss Hornbostel," he admitted shamefacedly, "I guess the jig is up."

"Tell her, you swine!" grunted Russell menacingly, pounding his windward kidney.

"I—I am Jim the Penman," said Fothergill with bowed head. "I forged the notes which sent your father, Harry Trefusis, to the cooler."

"Then you are Donald Fenstermacher, Russell?" I queried, dazed. He put his strong young arms about me and nodded shyly.

"Now may I ask you that question?" he blushed.

"Yes, Donald," I told him, hiding my scarlet face in his shoulder. Outside, the insupportable sweetness of a guitar cleft the warm summer air and bewhiskered, beflanneled, bejasused and bejabered undergraduates strolled under the hoary elms. The Splendid Wayfarer had come home.

TO SLEEP,
PERCHANCE TO STEAM

To anybody around here who is suffering from a touch of insomnia these days (surely no more than a hundred-to-one shot), the sequence of events in my bedroom last night may have a certain clinical interest. About nine o'clock, after a brisk session with the newscasters, I shuddered for approximately half an hour to relax my nerves, plugged a pair of Flents into my ears, and tied on a sleep mask. I probably should have waited until I got into bed before doing so, as I took a rather nasty fall over a waste-basket, but in a few moments I was stretched out, busily reviewing the war news and adding up the family bank account, with my pulse furnishing a rich musical background. When this palled, I read several chapters of Durfee's "Monasteries of the Rhône" with no success whatever until I discovered I had forgotten to remove my mask. As soon as I did, I was amply rewarded, for I found that with a little practice I was able to handle the strategy of the war and add up my bank account while vagabonding down the Rhône.

At this point, I regret to say, I tarnished an otherwise perfect record by falling into a slight doze. I must have been asleep almost fifteen minutes when I awoke suddenly and realized I had neglected to take a sedative before retiring. I promptly went out into the kitchen for a cup of hot milk with which to dissolve the nepenthe tablet and found Delia, our buxom cook, seated on the knee of her policeman friend. Actually, we have no cook called

Delia, but we do have an impassive Englishman named Crichton and he was seated on the knee of a police-woman. The general effect was the same: a scene of coarse, steamy intimacy rivalling Hogarth's "Gin Lane." Muttering "This rivals Hogarth's 'Gin Lane'," I stalked back to bed just in time to discover that the annual outing of the Clan-na-Gael was beginning directly beneath my window. Egged on by shrill cries of approval from the ladies' auxiliary, strapping bosthoons executed nimble jigs and reels, sang come-all-ye's, and vied with each other in hurling refuse cans the length of the street. The gaiety was so spontaneous and impulsive that I could not refrain from distributing several bags of water as favors. The gesture moved the crowd deeply, a few of its members even offering to come up and include me in their horse-play. Unfortunately, my good-natured refusal caused considerable pique and the revellers disbanded shortly. The sky and I were turning gray when, without any preamble, a woman in the apartment directly overhead began beating her husband mercilessly. Unable to withstand his screams, I finally gathered up all the available bedding, wrapped my head in it, and lay in a cedar chest in the foyer until routed out by the odor of coffee.

It is the notion of the General Electric Company, as set forth in a booklet I picked up at Lewis & Congers's Sleep Shop later in the morning, that this sordid series of events need never have occurred had I only been equipped with a recent discovery of theirs. Some anonymous genius in Schenectady (who will yet turn out to be Paul Muni, mark my words) has conjured up from his alembics and

131

retorts an electrical comforter known as "The Blanket with a Brain." Just how General Electric came to be mixed up in blanket research is not too clear; perhaps it was one of those accidents we know take place daily in laboratories. I can readily imagine some brilliant young chemist bursting into the office of the head of the division, exultantly waving an Erlenmeyer flask. "What's cooking, Shaftoe—I mean Muni?" inquires his chief irritably. "Another one of those impractical daydreams of yours?" "N-n-no, sir," stammers Shaftoe in his excitement. "Do you recall that precipitate of blanketane, comfortate cellulose, and old voltage I left on my bench last night?" "Yes, it was the seven-hundred-and-forty-fifth combination you and Bazurdjian had tried, and although all the others failed, you doggedly persisted, scorning the mockery of older and wiser heads," replies the chief. "Look here, sir!" cries Shaftoe, holding the flask up to the light. "My God!" exclaims his usually imperturbable senior. "A little electrical quilt! Imperfect, incomplete, picayune, but still a quilt! What formula did you use, my boy?" "A very old one, sir," says Shaftoe quietly. "One part inspiration and ten of perspiration." "Success hasn't changed you, Shaftoe," observes the chief. "You're still a drip." And, pocketing the discovery, he kicks Shaftoe out into the corridor.

Outwardly, the G. E. Electric Comforter is a simple wool-and-taffeta affair which runs on the house current and automatically adjusts itself to the changing temperatures of the night. What emerges from a study of the booklet, however, is a weird complex of thermostats, transformers, and control boxes likely to frighten the putative customer out of his pants. "The heart of the Comforter," states the booklet, "is a web of 370 feet of fine flexible copper wire of low resistance arranged in a zigzag pattern." Set me down as a dusty old eccentric, but frankly, there would seem to be some more ideal haven nowadays than a skein of copper wire, no matter how fine or flexible. Nor is it any more reassuring to learn that "six rubber molded safety thermostats are placed at intervals in this web of insulated wire (you can feel these thermostats with your fingers beneath the cover of the Comforter)." It needs no vivid imagination to imagine oneself lying in the dark with eyes protruding, endlessly tallying the thermostats and expecting at any moment to be converted into roast Long Island duckling. The possibility is evidently far from academic, to judge from the question a little later on: "Can the Comforter overheat or give an electric shock?" The manufacturers shrug aside the contingency in a breezy 450-word essay, easily comprehensible to wizards like Steinmetz but unhappily just out of my reach. One passage, nevertheless, is all too succinct:

Even if the full 115 volts went through the Comforter, the body would have to be moist . . . a worn spot on the web wire inside the Comforter would have to touch the body . . . and another part of the body, as a hand or leg, would have to come in contact with a piece of metal, in order to get the sensation of an electric shock.

Given half a chance, I know I could fulfill these conditions, difficult though they seem. As one who puts on a pair of rubbers when he changes a fuse, only to find himself recumbent on the floor with his eyelashes singed, I'll go further. I bet I could pass through a room containing an Electric Comforter in the original gift box and emerge with a third-degree burn.

The balance of the booklet, to tell the truth, held for me a purely formal interest, as I had already reached a decision regarding the Comforter. Such questions as "What causes the slight clicking noise in the control box?" are obviously intended to relieve the fears of neurotics, and, thank God, I'm no neurotic. All I know is, when I got that far I heard a slight clicking noise and experienced a distinct tingling sensation which could only have emanated from the booklet itself. Luckily, I had the presence of mind to plunge it into a pail of water and yell for help. Right now it's over at some expert's office, about to be analyzed. And so am I, honey, if I can lay my hands on a good five-cent psychiatrist.

DOWN WITH THE
RESTORATION!

Does anybody here mind if I make a prediction? I haven't made a prediction since the opening night of *The Women* some years ago, when I rose at the end of the third act and announced to my escort, a Miss Chicken-Licken, "The public will never take this to its bosom." Since the public has practically worn its bosom to a nubbin niggling up to *The Women*, I feel that my predictions may be a straw to show the direction the wind is blowing away from. I may very well open up a cave and do business as a sort of Cumaean Sibyl in reverse. You can't tell me people would rather climb up that Aventine Hill and have a man mess around with the entrails of a lot of sacred chickens when they can come down into my nice cool cave and get a good hygienic prediction for a few cents. So just to stimulate trade and start the ball rolling, here goes my first prediction: One of these days two young people are going to stumble across a ruined farmhouse and leave it alone. . . . Well, what are you sitting there gaping at? You heard what I said. That's my prediction.

Honest Injun, I hate to sound crotchety, and the last thing in the world I want to do is throw the editors of all those home-making magazines like *Nook and Garden* and *The American Home-Owner* into an uproar, but the plain fact is that I've got a bellyful. For over two years now, every time I start leafing through one of those excellent periodicals, I fall afoul of another article about a couple of young people who stumble across a ruined farm-house and remodel it on what is inelegantly termed spit and coupons. Or maybe it's the same article. I couldn't be reading the same issue over and over, could I?

All these remodelling articles are written by the re-modellers themselves and never by the ruined farmer or the man who didn't get paid for the plastering, which accounts for their rather smug tone. They invariably follow the same pattern. A young couple named Mibs and Evan (and if you checked up, I'll bet they were never married at *all!*) have decided to return to the land. I see Mibs as one of those girls on the short side, with stocky legs, a low-slung posterior, and an untidy bun of straw-colored hair continually unwinding on the nape of her neck. Before anyone ever heard of Salzburg, she wore a high-bodiced dress with full skirts, a sort of horrid super-dirndl with home-cooked hems that have a tendency to hang down in back. She is usually engaged in reading a book written by two unfrocked chemists which tells women how to make their own cold cream by mixing a little potash with a dram of glycerine and a few cloves. Evan is a full-haunched young man in a fuzzy woollen suit (I don't suppose there's any such thing as a fuzzy cotton suit, but you know what I mean) who is forever rubbing a briar pipe along his nose to show you the beauty of the grain. He smokes his own mixture of perique, Latakia, and Imperial Cube Cut, for the very good reason that nobody else will smoke it, and he has probably read more of Arthur Machen than any man alive.

Well, as I say, your average remodelling yarn begins

with Mibs and Evan stumbling across the most adorable ruin of an eighteenth-century farmhouse. It doesn't *have* to be a farmhouse; it can be a gristmill, or a tobacco barn, or a Mennonite schoolhouse. It can even be an early Colonial hen house, with delightful hand-hewn beams and perfectly sweet old tar paper scaling off the sides. Apparently nobody previous to Mibs and Evan has realized its possibilities, but Evan takes one look at it and says in a guarded tone, "Two hundred dollars would restore that beautifully if you didn't go crazy putting in a lot of bathrooms you didn't need." "Oh, Evan!" breathes Mibs, her eyes shining above her adenoids and her brain reeling with visions of Cape Cod spatter floors. "Dare we . . . ?" That night, at dinner in the Jumble Shop, they put their heads together—Evan removes the pipe from alongside his nose, of course—and decide to jump at the chance. It involves giving up that trip to Europe, a choice the characters in these stories always have to make, but Mibs has always dreamed of a sunny garden filled with old-fashioned flowers of the type her mother used to read about in Max Schling's catalogue. So they bravely draw two hundred dollars out of their little hoard, leaving a hundred in case they ever want to take a really long trip to some place like Bali, and lay it on the line.

After considerable excitement, in which everybody searches the title like mad and Mibs discovers the quaintest old parchment deed describing their land in terms of rods, chains, and poods, they are ready to take the "Before" snapshots. Evan digs up one of the cameras used by Brady at the battle of Antietam, waits for a good cloudy day, and focuses across a mound of guano at the most ramshackle corner of the "manse," as Mibs calls it with irreverent mischief. The article generally carries several gray smudges captioned "Southwest corner of the house before work began," and you can't help wondering where those giant oaks came from in the "After" photographs. Maybe they sprang up from acorns dropped by the workmen while they were having lunch.

The first thing the high-hearted pair decide on is a new roof. This fortunately costs only eight dollars, as they use second-hand wattles and hire a twelve-year-old scab—all right, maybe he only mislaid his union card—to tack them on. The outside walls are a problem, but an amazing stroke of good fortune comes to their rescue. Opening a trap door they hadn't investigated, Mibs and Evan stumble across countless bundles of lovely old hand-split shingles which have been overlooked by previous tenants, like the hens. Two superb Adam fireplaces, hitherto concealed by some matchboarding, now make their appearance, in one of them a box of dusty but otherwise well-preserved pieces of Sandwich and Stiegel glass. "The attic!" shout Mibs and Evan simultaneously, suddenly remembering their resolution to look through it some rainy day, and sure enough, there they find a veritable treasure trove of pewter ware, cherry escritoires, Chippendale wing chairs, sawbuck tables, and Field beds, hidden away by survivors of the Deerfield massacre. "It just didn't seem *possible*," recalls Mibs candidly, up to her old trick of taking the words out of your mouth.

And now, suddenly, the place becomes a hive of activity. A salty old character named Lafe (who is really Paul Bunyan, no matter what *Nook and Garden* says) appears and does the work of ten men at the price of one. He pulls down trees with his bare hands, lays new floors, puts up partitions, installs electricity, diverts streams, forges the ironware, bakes porcelain sinks, and all but spins silk for the draperies. How this djinn ever escaped from his bottle, and where he is now, the article neglects to mention. The upshot is that in a little over two weeks, the last hooked rug—picked up by Mibs at an auction for ten cents after spirited bidding—is in place and the early Salem kettle is singing merrily on the hob. A fat orange tabby blinks before the fire and Evan, one arm around Mibs, is adding up a column of figures. "Think of it, lover," whispers Mibs with dancing eyes. "We did the whole thing for only *fifty-one dollars and eighteen cents!*" "Less than we'll get for that article in *The American Home-Owner*," murmurs Evan exultantly, reaming the cake from his pipe. "Tell me, does oo love its 'ittle—" . . . And now would you hate me if I stole out very quietly? I'm afraid there's going to be just a wee bit of baby talk.

THE BODY BEAUTIFUL

Sometimes when I have worked for hours in vain over a difficult problem in Baker Street and my keen hawklike profile is drawn with fatigue, I like to take down my Stradivarius, pile it on the fire and curl up with a cop of *Hygeia*, the monthly magazine published by the American Medical Association. I don't necessarily have to read it; all I have to do is curl up with it. In a few minutes my pulse becomes normal, my eyes glaze over, and I am ready to do business with the Sandman. I don't know much about medicine but I know what I like. If the American Medical Association would only put up this magazine in tablet or powder form nobody would ever pass a white night again. Unlike other soporifics, *Hygeia* does not affect the heart; I have even read a copy without any ill effects other than a feeling of drowsiness the next day. It fulfills every requirement of the United States Pharmacopeia; it is clean, it is fresh every month, and it is standard strength. From the opening essay on flat feet down to the very last article on diabetic muffins, it is a guaranteed yawn from cover to cover.

The one oasis in this Sahara, however, is a sort of out-patient clinic where the layman is allowed to make a fool of himself in full view of the medical profession. I quote at random (random hell, I had to look through nineteen copies to find it) a letter headed "Synthetic Saliva" appearing in the Q. and A. department of *Hygeia*:

"To the Editor:—How could saliva be duplicated?

Where could the proper materials be secured to duplicate it or nearly so?—H.C.D., Illinois.

Here is a cry from the heart. Obviously some young Frankenstein has built himself a monster or Golem in his spare time out in the woodshed. With infinite labor and utmost secrecy, using bits of wire, tin, old bones and meat, he has created the perfect robot. Suddenly, on the verge of completion, he stops in sudden panic. He has left out saliva. The monster is beginning to growl ominously; he wants what all the other boys on the street have. But do you think the editors of *Hygeia* care? They fob off H.C.D. (possibly one of the most brilliant inventors of our time) with a few heavy-duty medical words and sink into a complacent snooze, unmindful that a raging monster with a dry mouth may be loose in the Middle West at this very moment. I don't like to be an alarmist, fellows, but this is a very short-sighted attitude.

No matter how blasé they imagine themselves, hypochondriacs from six to sixty will get a deep and ghoulish satisfaction studying the correspondence which appears each month. Those private maladies you have been pruning and transplanting couldn't possibly compare with the things that bother *Hygeia* readers. The pathetic query of J.I.B., Pennsylvania, will illustrate:

"To the Editor:—Is there any danger of contracting radium poisoning from the use of clocks painted with a radium compound; for instance, in case the clock crystal should be broken and the radium compound chipped off?"

The editors, who pretend to know everything, reply

that there is no danger whatsoever. This is pretty cold comfort to a man who probably glows like a Big Ben every time he enters a dark room. However, he might as well stop barking up the wrong tree; he wouldn't get a civil answer from *Hygeia* even if he grew a minute hand and sounded the hour and half-hour with a musical chime.

I would like to think that the case of G.S., Ohio, is also one of hypochondria but it has a more ominous ring:

"To the Editor:—Can the statements contained in a recent daily newspaper that bobbing the hair will cause girls to grow beards be verified? Or is it just a bit of propaganda?"

If that isn't a tacit admission that Miss G.S. is sporting a grogan or an imperial around Ohio, I knock under. Even if she only *thinks* she has a beard, I wouldn't give her house-room; but that is beside the point, as she has not asked me for house-room. She probably has the whole house to herself anyway. Much more understandable is the plight of the frightened Kansan who writes as follows:

"To the Editor:—My students tell me that surgeons have been able to transplant the stomach from an animal, as a calf or a goat, into man. Is this possible?—N.B.Z., Kansas."

I can sympathize with the poor fellow for I, too, get the same sensation when I drink black velvet. Actually, it only *feels* as if you had changed stomachs with a goat. One morning I even woke up convinced that I had swallowed a marble the night before. To make it worse, a man named Mr. Coffee-Nerves was standing over my bed in a white Prince Albert, helping me to hate myself. I got up and went right through him to the bathroom where I had a long look at my chest. At first I couldn't tell whether it was a steelie or a bull's-eye, but it turned out to be a clear glass agate with a little lamb inside. I managed to dissolve my marble with two aspirins in a glass of hot water. But thank God I'm no hypochondriac; you don't catch me writing letters to the American Medical Association.

For a refreshing contrast to *Hygeia*, one turns to a live-wire little monthly called *Estes Back to Nature Magazine*, published at 113 North LaBrea Avenue, Hollywood, California. Its editor is Dr. St. Louis Estes, who modestly styles himself "Discoverer of Brain Breathing and Dynamic Breath Controls for Disease Prevention and Life Extension, Father and Founder of the Raw Food Movement, and International Authority on Old Age and Raw Foods." (There is something to write on a library card when they ask you for your occupation.) Cooked vegetables, spices, and hair tonic are poison, says Dr. Estes, and although I have never tried the combination, I can readily believe it. But the Doctor is constructive, and I know no better answer to the cynicism and bigotry of *Hygeia* than a menu I found in his magazine. It was labelled "A Dinner Fit for a King" and it still haunts me:

"EGG AND FRUIT SOUP: To one quart of milk and one pint of cream, beat in thoroughly four eggs. Use as a filler cubed pineapple, sweeten to taste with honey. Serve in cups like broth.

"MOCK TURKEY—WHITE MEAT: Into one pound of cottage cheese mix and roll equal amount of raw flaked pecans, peanuts and jordan almonds. until it becomes a thick, solid mass. Season to taste with chopped onions, pimientos, green peppers, adding a dash of powdered celery, sage and horseradish. Serve in slices like white meat.

"MAPLE ICE CREAM: To one pint of whipped cream add one pint of pure maple syrup. Whip until thick. Then add the beaten whites of two eggs and one cupful of chopped nuts. Freeze."

I froze.

POISONOUS MUSHROOMS

Are We at the Crossroads?

Well, autumn is here again, and very shortly every Tom, Dick and Harry will be asking himself the question "Poisonous mushrooms—yes or no?" In every mossy dell, in every nook of granny, these delicious little edibles are springing up. Only yesterday I happened to fall into conversation with a stranger in the subway, an extremely well-made woman of thirty-one with Dresden-dainty hands and feet. I noticed that she was eating a small umbrella-shaped object and asked her what it was.

"An umbrella," she replied shortly, descending from the train at Seventy-second Street. Needless to say, the incident did not pass unnoticed, and I retired in confusion amid the hearty laughter of several wealthy cattle-drovers who had come down to New York for the day on the steam cars.

I first became interested in mushrooms about ten years ago. Two friends of mine named Johnny had a little place, a sort of cellar, on Fifty-second Street where they kept coal and wood and ice. I was down there one evening bent on some coal and wood when Tony pointed to the ceiling and said "*Corpo di Bacco*, what's *that*?" I looked up and there was a whole clump of mushrooms growing right out at me. Well, I let out a scream fit to wake a dead man—as a matter of fact, it *did* wake up a dead man who'd been in the corner for three days and he came over and tried to bite me. As I say, I stayed in bed nearly two weeks that time, but after I was well, I got this Frank and Johnny to put aside the place as a sort of permanent laboratory where I could study the mushrooms.

It will probably come as a mild shock to no one that there are all of four hundred different kinds of mushrooms. Four hundred and one, really, because when I looked up this fact in the *World Almanac*, I found a new variety growing out of Page 29. Now, what are mushrooms? Nothing more or less than toadstools, though why they are called toadstools is beyond me; I have yet to see a toad sitting on a stool, although I have combed all the books dealing with the subject. Of course I haven't had a chance to study the books yet—all I've been able to do is comb them, but still, it seems a peculiar name to give an unoffending mushroom, doesn't it? It was probably made up by someone who hated mushrooms and thought he could get even. But why should anybody hate mushrooms? The little fellow goes about his business quietly; once in a while he kills a family of twenty or thirty people, but then, what right has anyone to have a family of twenty or thirty people? I was wrapping up some laundry in a newspaper recently and saw a note about a man who had had thirty children. This sort of thing can't go on indefinitely, no matter what the man says.

In the eleven years I have been studying mushrooms at my laboratory on Fifty-second Street, I have seen cases of almost uncanny intelligence among my specimens. I had a Peppery Lactarius growing in a glass right next to a Fistulina Hepatica, or Beefsteak Mushroom. (If you can imagine a purple beefsteak covered with short prickly spines growing out of a tree, you will easily see why science chose this name, and you can then explain it to me.) Well, one morning I made the rounds of my collection and found that during the night Miss Peppery Lactarius had moved into Mr. Beefsteak Mushroom's jar. I woke up my assistant, put a little ice on his head, and quizzed him. But no; he had been right there on the floor since eleven-thirty the night before. To this day we have never been able to solve the riddle, and it is still referred to by superstitious folk in the neighborhood as "The Mystery of the Migrating Mushrooms." I am thinking of bringing it out in book form, perhaps adding a mysterious puffy toadstool in a black hat who was seen skulking near by.

But how to tell the poisonous mushroom from the harmless variety, since both are found in the same localities, have the same habits, and the same dull look around the face? Ah—don't be surprised—the mushroom has a face, and if you look very closely and carefully, you will see the merest hint of an eye, two noses, and a lip. For purposes of identification, we have what we call the Alfred Zeigler test, named after Professor Schaffner of the University of Rochester. The mushrooms are boiled for twenty minutes and their jackets removed. They are then placed in a frying pan with a cubic centimeter of butter, a gram of pepper, and a penny-weight of coarse salt, after which they are subjected to 137 degrees of heat Fahrenheit in the laboratory oven, removed, and placed on antiseptic paper plates. Fifteen minutes after they are eaten, a reaction will be noted. If the mushrooms are harmless, the subject will want to lie down, remove his or her collar, and roll over on his or her face. If poisonous, the balance of the mushrooms should be thrown out, as they are unfit to consume.

The mushroom often turns up in some really remarkable forms. Sir Joseph Mushroom, from whom their name is derived, tells an interesting anecdote. A cask of wine had been left undisturbed in a cellar for three years, in some country other than the United States. At the end of that time, the cask was found firmly fastened to the ceiling by a large mushroom which had grown as the wine leaked out. The cask was quite empty when found, and how the mushroom looked was nobody's business. Sir Joseph, by the way, no longer raises mushrooms; he has settled down quietly in Surrey, where he devotes himself to raising bees, but there is still a reminiscent gleam in his eye when Irene Adler is mentioned.

Little else remains to be told. Fred Patton, the former Erie train boy, still continues to rise in Mr. Proskauer's mercantile establishment on Ann Street, and Gloria Proskauer blushes prettily whenever Fred's name is uttered. This, however, is all too seldom, as the unfortunate Fred was hit in the vertical cervix by a baked apple last New Year's Day and succumbed almost instantly. And so we leave the little snitch right smack up behind the eight-ball, and a good end for the mealy-mouthed, psalm-singing petty thief, if you ask me.

BUTTON, BUTTON, WHO'S GOT THE BLEND?

About eight o'clock last night I was lounging at the corner of Hollywood Boulevard and Vine Street, an intersection celebrated in the eclogues of Louella Parsons and Ed Sullivan, waiting for a pert baggage who had agreed to accompany me to a double feature. If I bore myself with a certain assurance, it was because I had chosen my wardrobe with some care—a shower-of-hail suit, lilac gloves, a split-sennit boater, and a light whangee cane. Altogether, I had reason for self-satisfaction; I had dined famously off a charmburger and a sky-high malt, my cigar was drawing well, and the titles of the pictures I was about to witness, "Block That Kiss" and "Khaki Buck-aroo," augured gales of merriment. For a moment high spirits tempted me to invest in a box of maxixe cherries or fondant creams for my vis-à-vis, but after due reflection I fought back the impulse. How utterly cloying, how anti-climactic sweets would be after the speeches I had in store for the pretty creature!

Weary at last of studying the colorful throng eddying past me (I had already singled out Eddy Duchin, Sherwood Eddy, Eddie Cantor, Nelson Eddy, and Eddie Robinson), I fell to examining a nearby billboard. The advertisement was one of that familiar type in which an entire cross section of the population seems to be rhapsodizing about the product—in this case, a delicacy named Hostess Cup Cakes. "You should hear my bridge club rave about those Hostess Cup Cakes," an excited housewife was babbling to her friend, whose riposte was equally feverish: "I wouldn't dare pack John's lunch without putting in Hostess Cup Cakes!" Close by, a policeman smiled benignly at a baby in a carriage, addressing its mother with, "You have a lot of time for 'Precious' these afternoons, Mrs. Jones." The reason for Mrs. Jones' leisure was not unpredictable: "That's because it's easy to plan desserts with Hostess Cup Cakes." The baby itself was making no contribution to the symposium; apparently the kitten had got hold of its tongue, but you could tell from its expression that it would creep a mile for a cup cake. It was, however, with a dialogue between two small boys that the copywriter kindled my interest into flame. "Hurry!" one of them was admonishing the other. "I've got 5c for Hostess Cup Cakes!" "Oh, boy!" chortled his companion. "Do I love that *secret chocolate blend!*"

Although the romantic possibilities of a secret chocolate blend and its theft by the spies of an enemy power are undeniable, I think that behind the phrase there lurks a warmer, more personal story. Naturally, the brief harlequinade which follows can indicate no more than its highlights, but if the Hostess Cup Cake people care to endow me for the next few months, I could expand it into a three-act version, suitable for annual presentation at Hollywood and Vine. I have no further use for that corner, or, may I add, for my *petite amie*, who turned up sobbing drunk with a Marine on either arm.

(Scene: *The office of Dirk van Bensdorp, president and general manager of the Hostess Cup Cake Corporation.*

As the curtain rises, Dirk, a forceful executive, is reading a lecture to his ne'er-do-well nephew, Jan Gluten, a minor employee of the firm. The latter fidgets nervously with an icing gun. His eyes are puffy with lack of sleep and the little lines radiating from his nose attest eloquently to fondness for the grape.)

DIRK (warningly)—Now, look here, my boy, I'm going to talk to you like a Dutch uncle. Bakery circles are abuzz with your escapades. You had better mend your ways ere I lose patience.

JAN (surlily)—Aw, can de sermon.

DIRK—It's a stench in the nostrils of the cup-cake trade —throwing away your guilders on fly chorus girls and driving your Stutz Bearcat in excess of sixty M.P.H.

JAN (lighting a cigarette with nicotine-stained fingers) —I'm getting sick of dis joint. Every time I take a schnapps or two wit' de fellers, some willy boy splits on me to de front office.

DIRK (severely)—It's your work that gives you away, my fine fellow. That last tray of fig bars you frosted was a botch!

JAN (lamely)—Dere was a fly in de amber icing.

DIRK—Excuses, excuses! Why, the complaints I've had about your work would almost fill a book. (He holds up a book almost filled with complaints about Jan's work, a first edition.) And what's this about the attentions you have been paying a certain raven-haired miss in the custard division?

JAN (*fiercely*)—You keep Lorene Flake's name out of dis, d'ye hear?

DIRK (*aside*)—I see I have touched the lad in a vulnerable spot. This seems to be more than mere philandering.

JAN—Lorene's decent, and clean, and—and fine! She's straight as a string, I tell you!

DIRK (*who loves a good joke now and then*)—That's probably why you're "knots" about her—ha-ha-ha!

JAN—Sharrap.

DIRK (*earnestly*)—Why not prove yourself to the girl, Jan? Eschew your dubious associates and turn over a new chocolate leaf.

JAN—Hully gee, I ain't fit to kiss de cuff of her slacks.

DIRK—Do your job and you'll win through. Make the cup cakes fly under your fingers!

JAN (*cynically*)—Aw, rats. Youse is attempting to fob off de speed-up system under de cloak of benevolent paternalism. (*He exits.*)

DIRK—Ah, well, there's good stuff in the boy. I was the same at his age. (*Ten Eyck, the shop foreman, bursts in, his face ashen.*)

TEN EYCK (*panting*)—The formula—

DIRK—What is it, man? What's happened?

TEN EYCK—The secret chocolate blend—gone—stolen!

DIRK (*sputtering*)—Ten thousand devils! But I locked it in the safe myself last night!

TEN EYCK—I found the door wrenched off, beside it an acetylene torch and a complete set of burglar's tools.

DIRK (*instantly*)—Someone must have opened the safe by force! (*A heavy footfall is heard on the stair.*)

Ten Eyck—Why, who can that be?

Dirk—God grant that it may be Inspector Bunce, he who gave us such material assistance in that mysterious affair of the oatmeal cookies! (*His prayers are answered; Bunce enters, looks about him keenly*) Inspector, our secret choc—

Bunce—Yes, I know. When I find a safe pried open, a series of unfrosted cup cakes, and two middle-aged bakers in a notable state of agitation, the conclusions are fairly obvious.

Dirk—You mean that the finger of suspicion points to Loose-Wiles, the Thousand Window Bakeries, whose agents have recently been skulking about in dirty gray caps and gooseneck sweaters?

Bunce—This is an inside job, Bensdorp. I should like a few words with your nephew.

Dirk (*paling*)—Surely you don't believe Jan—

Bunce—Please be good enough to call him. (*Dirk, bewildered, presses a button and Jan shuffles in sullenly.*) Well, Gluten, still sticking to your story?

Jan (*sneering*)—I ain't got nuttin' else to add, see? I pinched de secret chocolate plans to pay for de extravagances of an actress I was infatuated wit'. It's an oft-told story, rendered none de less sordid by repetition.

Bunce (*with deadly calm*)—One moment. Why are you shielding Vernon Flake?

Jan (*roughly*)—I never heard of de cove. Come on, clap de darbies on me wrists. I'm ready to face de music.

Bunce—It won't wash, Jan. You found Vernon, Lorene's worthless brother, crouched before the safe and to protect the girl you love you have shouldered the blame yourself!

JAN (*modestly*)—Any bloke in me shoes would have done de equivalent.

DIRK—Hooray! I was convinced of his innocence at all times!

JAN (*producing a cinnamon bun*)—And here is de formula inside dis sweetmeat, where de luckless Vernon hid it for safekeeping.

BUNCE—You've a smart cub there, Bensdorp. Nephews of his stripe don't grow on trees. (*Reaching for his Persian slipper*) Well, Ten Eyck, what do you say to Sarasate at the Albert Hall tonight, eh?

TEN EYCK—Capital, my dear Bunce. (*They exit.*)

DIRK (*embracing Jan*)—Well, you young rascal, you shall have your reward for this. Henceforth our Friday specials will be known as "Cub Cakes" in your honor—and remember, there's always room for brains at the top in this organization.

JAN (*surreptitiously pocketing his uncle's stickpin*)—You said a mout'ful, cul.

CURTAIN

BOY MEETS GIRL
MEETS FOOT

Anybody who chanced to be flatboating down the Sunday book-review sections lately, poling his way through such nifties as *Bismarck: A New Synthesis*, by Dr. Stauffer, or *A Deciduous Girl of Old Williamsburgh*, by Sara Leamington Latrobe, probably wound up the day in a darkened room applying vinegar poultices freely to his forehead. It would seem from the publishers' spring lists that the entire Hippocratic fraternity had forsworn the art of healing in favor of letters. Possibly because of the general world breakdown, the family doctor whose reticence was celebrated in song and story has suddenly caved in and become a garrulous old chatterbox, buttonholing the passerby and babbling your most cherished anatomical secrets. Since the success of Dr. Victor Heiser, a veritable freshet of reminiscence has been roaring through the bookshops. If turnabout is fair play and a layman may diagnose his physician's complaint, the boys who wrote *The Horse and Buggy Doctor*, *Consultation Room*, and *Doctor, Here's Your Hat* are down with a thundering case of *furor scribendi*. Gone the spatula and the glittering optical mirror, and in their place the quill pen and the purple patch. If you have been looking for a bargain in second-hand scalpels, this is your golden opportunity. But it looks like a hell of a summer for invalids.

It remained for Dr. Dudley J. Morton of the College of Physicians and Surgeons at Columbia, however, to invest the common or garden foot with glamour and employ it as material for romance. In *Oh, Doctor! My Feet!* undeniably the most plaintive title of the season, Dr. Morton sets your foot tapping, if only to convince yourself that it still articulates. Dr. Morton has builded better than he knew; the reader becomes so acutely aware of his feet that he spends his day listening with a rather cunning expression to his toes meshing into gear. My experience has been that although this type of work is not exhausting, it pays very badly.

Dr. Morton, with a sense of dramatic value not commonly encountered in orthopedists, opens his narrative explosively. Into the office of a Dr. Nelson, shouting, "Oh, Doctor! *My feet!*" bursts Mrs. Roberts, an attractive young matron. Conscious of the brusqueness of her words, she adds hastily, "Oh, please forgive me, Dr. Nelson, but my feet burn and ache so I scarcely know what to do." Dr. Nelson soothingly guides her to a chair with, "Well, you have done the rational thing by coming to see me, for I'm certain I can help you." I suppose the irrational thing for Mrs. Roberts would have been to consult a blacksmith, but I myself would have liked her better for it. As a matter of fact, Dr. Morton throughout portrays Mrs. Roberts as something of a creep, which I suspect is a deep-seated conviction among doctors about their patients. She is scarcely seated when her face expresses "a considerable degree of surprise." "Why, I didn't know you were interested in feet, Doctor." By one of those amazing coincidences which happen only in fiction, Dr. Nelson turns out to be the ideal party to whom Mrs. Roberts should have brought her feet. He invites her to relate her symptoms. "Well, Doctor," Mrs. Roberts replies, "they started to bother me about two years ago and since then I've tried almost everything. My closet is so full of shoes I've bought on recommendation or seen advertised that my husband laughs at me and suggests I open a store." You will notice that Dr. Morton, not content with delineating Mrs. Roberts as a simpleton, gratuitously insinuates her husband is a red-faced, bull-necked extrovert who taunts his wife with her malady. Somehow, it left me with the uncomfortable feeling that the author had poisoned a well. Try as I would, I kept seeing Mr. Roberts in my mind's eye as a sort of Dr. Grimesby Roylott, a savage tyrant who goes around kicking open doors and bending pokers double.

Oddly enough, at this very juncture Dr. Nelson puts on a display of scientific deduction that would have done credit to Holmes himself. Ordering Mrs. Roberts to remove her shoes and stockings and stand directly in front of him, he asks his patient, with hardly more than a cursory glance, "Do you have the calluses on the soles of your feet treated often?" If Mrs. Roberts was surprised before, she now is reduced to a stupefaction worthy of Watson. "You haven't even looked at the bottom of my feet," she reminds the Doctor faintly. The latter, without even a casual yawn, points out that her second toes are distinctly longer than her great toes. Simpering girlishly, Mrs. Roberts replies, "But I always took that to be an indication of a perfect foot. If you will permit a little confession, I have always been secretly proud of my feet— at least, I have been since I noticed that the short great toe is distinctly shown in Grecian sculpture." Dr. Nelson, in that maddening way doctors have, crushes Mrs. Roberts' pitiful little pride in her feet with the rejoinder, "What was ideal for the women of ancient Greece is definitely not ideal for the modern woman who wears high-heeled shoes." Of course, old smarty-pants Nelson knows what Grecian women wore on their feet; he was there. Everybody remembers *him* around the agora, arm in arm with Pericles. Oh, you wine-dark, loud-thundering, many-throated Nelson, you!

Well, one thing and another and before you know it Mrs. Roberts is on her way home with orders to stay off her feet and plunge them alternately into hot and cold water, which I could have told her who know as much about podiatry as any wide-awake gibbon in the Bronx Park Zoo.

The next chapter is a colloquy on Mrs. Roberts' feet between the Doctor and his nurse. This could easily be lifted in its entirety and put into a revue. The dialogue is crisp and meaty, and Dr. Nelson manages to make quite a fool of the girl with his answers. It would have made an effective blackout had they beaten each other with rolled-up newspapers, but there I go carping again. Early next morning another patient staggers in, a Mrs. Wells. She, too, is having a very thin time with her feet, and the Doctor treats her with the tender sympathy of a Torquemada: "He then proceeded to test the movements of all the joints of the foot and ankle, noting that Mrs. Wells was able, when her knees were held straight, to bend her feet upward only slightly beyond a right angle with her legs. [That is, without applying the boot.] Finally he pressed gently but deeply into the centre of her instep. She winced and drew her foot back, just as Mrs. Roberts had done the day before." The upshot of this diablerie is one of those superb bits of patient-baiting that doctors excel at: "His patient . . . could no longer suppress her eager curiosity. 'Doctor,' she asked, 'are my arches fallen?' 'No,' he replied, 'they aren't—any more than a person with eyestrain is blind.' " In her place I would have given the Doctor a jab in the sweetbreads with my shiv and trusted my feet, however retrograde, to outrun the law. But Mrs. Wells, shaken by her session on the rack, has hardly strength to whimper. With the admonition she is to rest her feet and take contrast plunges—old sure-shot Nelson—Mrs. Wells totters out, her nerves vibrating like mandolin strings.

From this point on, I must confess, the suspense implicit in the characters is not sustained. With all the elements of a corking triangle, two women driven crazy by their feet and their love for a handsome orthopedist, the author does little. True, he has Dr. Nelson afford his patients some relief, but at what a price! In the twelfth chapter, Mrs. Roberts confesses, "Dr. Nelson, my feet are so much better, but I am embarrassed over the ridiculous way I acted the other day." In other words, he has succeeded in substituting a nice expensive neurosis for what is, after all, only a housewife's occupational disease. Moreover, on the very next page is the alarming admission, "The doctor examined her feet again. He noted that the calluses had been removed and the areas covered with moleskin." Is Mrs. Roberts happier with an inferiority complex and feet that look like a pair of old football pants? That's her lookout. Me, I'll string along with hexerei. Where would a man pick up a lucky potato and the hair ball of an ox?

WHAT AM I DOING
AWAY FROM HOME?

When I was growing up in New Guinea, or coming of age in Samoa, or whatever the hell I was doing about the age of thirteen, I had occasion to spend a considerable part of my life in hotels. To this day the subtle bouquet of brass polish, hotel carpeting, and rubber plants does more to recall my youth than a dozen faded albums. Mind you, this is no bid for sympathy. I did all right, even if I was the youngest patient in the history of the Keeley Cure. At least I could hold up my end in a group of travelling men discussing the Raines Law, which is more than can be said for certain milksops at Groton and St. George's.

What little scar tissue I carry from those early experiences, however, leaps into bas-relief at a publication of the Pennsylvania Hotels Association called *Live*. Its high purpose, according to a foreword, is "to tell you a few things about hotels you may not know . . . to show you how well a hotel cares for its guests no matter when they arrive or how tired or hungry they are." Judging from one anecdote, it sets about it in a fairly oblique manner:

Many years ago a foreigner, the guest of a hotel, wanted something done to his dress coat. He summoned a maid, but, unable to speak English, could do nothing but indicate his wishes by drawing his hand across the waist of the coat. It seemed obvious that he wanted the coattails cut off and she was about to send for the valet. He protested, urging her to do the job. She procured a scissors, cut off the tails and sewed the

161

raw edges as best she could. When he returned, he was furious. Much later it turned out he only wanted the coattails pinned back—a job he could easily have done himself. To his credit, he goodnaturedly agreed the joke was on him.

There is an air of dreadful, inhuman gaiety about the tale that freezes the marrow in one's bones. What grim rigadoon was this foreigner about to attend that he must have his coat-tails pinned back, what concourse of ghouls? I can almost see the ghastly grin lighting up his sunken face—if you can call it a face—as he agreed that the joke was on him. I'll thank the Pennsylvania Hotels Association to omit these fiendish vignettes if they want my custom.

And they certainly do—passionately, unreservedly, for on Page 8 of their brochure they offer twenty-seven prizes for the best essay on "Why I Like to Stop at a Hotel." "If you have ever stopped at a hotel—even for one night —you are eligible for this contest," they urge. Well, kids, I stopped at a hotel one night a while back, and in Pennsylvania, too. Not only am I eligible, but now that I've got the floor, you just try to take it away from me. I don't want a prize; all I want is a hearing.

Some years ago a small gasket which controls the plumbing in my country home gave way without warning, and while the plumbers were awaiting a duplicate from Cartier's, I tied a foxtail to the radiator of my Jordan cabriolet and went touring. Night found me at a crossroads before a spacious establishment with a handsome mansard roof and the inviting legend "Snapper Suppers." With many a cry of "Oh, dem snapper suppers!" and "Oh, dat succulent spoon bread wid cloudy honey fresh out ob de hive!" I flung myself on the dollar-and-a-quarter table d'hôte. The snapper supper turned out to have been prefabricated in Camden, New Jersey, and, dulling my hunger with something called a "spamwich" and a cup of lava, I mounted to my room. It was dominated by the bed, a sizable Victorian affair with a mattress easily two inches thick. Anticipating that guests might want to read in bed, the management had thoughtfully strung a naked electric bulb twelve feet away from the ceiling. I read the *Hotel Men's Guide* until my eyes rolled around the counterpane like marbles, and then turned in. The light was scarcely off before the wicker furniture began a slow, sinister gavotte around the room, creaking and groaning like Foxe's *Book of Martyrs*. Simultaneously automobile headlights started flashing across the bay window opposite my bed, and I realized that Dead Man's Carrefour was in for a night of brisk traffic. I was lying there trying to distinguish the lady motorists by the way the brakes screeched on the curve, when the voices went into action in the bar below.

At first they were pitched in a low, rasping hum devoid of vowels, somewhat like Icelandic but more bestial. As time wore on they became interwoven with sharp cries and commands of "Glonfy!" and "Rehume!" None of the words was quite audible, and as a result I had to keep every faculty tense. For a while I courted the theory that a group of Mr. Joyce's admirers were reading aloud from *Finnegans Wake*, but suddenly somebody started to break the spindles out of the back of a Windsor chair, using an

163

old-fashioned brass spittoon. I pounded on the floor; he cheerily beat an answering tattoo on the ceiling. I now decided to put my faith in the barbiturates, let the chips fall where they might, and swallowing several capsules that would have killed me had I been a horse, I crept back into my burrow.

A delightful surprise awaited me. Some sort of foreign body inside the pillow now insisted on obtruding into the back of my neck, a space ordinarily reserved for the caresses of wealthy middle-aged women. The obstruction seemed to be cylindrical, yielding to the touch, and about two and a half inches long—in short, the exact size and consistency of a roll of bills. The more I thought about it, the more convinced I became that I had unwittingly stumbled across a cache. And if size meant anything, the world was mine. I exultantly began planning how I would track down Baron Danglars, what I would do to Mercedes the fair Catalan. All that remained was to open the pillow. Any fool can open a pillow, I cackled.

It took me twenty minutes to realize that here was one fool who couldn't, armed with nothing more than a toothbrush, a comb and a commode. I hacked and tore at the seams of that pillow until my fingertips bled and I sobbed aloud with vexation. Meanwhile, in the bar below, the *Walpurgisnacht* was in full swing. On the stairs outside my room they were re-enacting Israel Putnam's escape from the British, and every so often somebody in the room overhead broke into a waltz clog in a pair of specially built lead shoes. Whether it was frustration, Sedormid, or both which finally got me, I'll never know. But this I do know: from now on I'm strictly the Scholar Gipsy, with a knapsack and a bit of bread and cheese snapping at my heels. It may be hot in a haystack, but by God, it's private.

HOLD THAT
CHRISTMAS TIGER!

About ten years ago there was translated to the screen as a vessel for the talents of Warner Baxter a play called "I Loved You Wednesday." The result was an amiable little film which undoubtedly recovered its investment, earned a snug profit, and in the normal course of things was retired to be cut into mandolin picks. What makes it still verdant in the memory of connoisseurs, however, is a patch of dialogue that came about the end of the first reel. Mr. Baxter, in beautifully tailored breeches and cordovans, had been established as a construction engineer on a vast, unidentified power project, barking crisp commands at giant cranes and chivying steam shovels. The scene then dissolved to his home, and as the workworn engineer entered, his wife looked up eagerly from her sewing. "What's new, dear?" she inquired. "Well, darling," replied Baxter, inhaling deeply and brushing clouds of alkali from his shoulders, "I just finished Boulder Dam." "Oh, *Jim!*" murmured his wife adoringly.

It may be presumptuous of me to compare myself in any sense with Mr. Baxter (I am twenty pounds lighter, not quite as photogenic, and infinitely less solvent), but if sheer doggedness and fighting heart mean anything, the undertaking I have just completed may yet outclass his. At ten o'clock this morning, fortified with a bottle of benzedrine and a stoup of black coffee, I kissed my newsdealer good-bye and set out to read through the Christmas-party suggestions in *Mademoiselle*, *Vogue* and *House & Gar-*

den. "It's madness, Derek!" implored the handful of friends who had come down to see me off. "Think it over, old man! You'll never get through!" I smiled grimly, set my jaw as well as a serious case of malocclusion would allow, and plunged into the perfume advertising. Hours later, gray with fatigue and my eyes mere pin-points in my head, I stumbled out of the back cover of *House & Garden* and fell forward into the waiting arms of my friends.

Perhaps the most soaring imagination displayed in any of the three magazines is that of a Mr. Lester Gaba, whom *Mademoiselle* called in to advise its readers regarding their Christmas décor. It is Mr. Gaba's thesis that, given a little energy and a few everyday materials, Christmas need never be stodgy. His first target is the tree itself. "Dip tips of twisted cotton strips into India ink and trim your tree entirely with 'ermine tails,'" he orders. "Pin a fresh mauve orchid to the treetop." Arresting as the effect might be, the actual execution seems a bit less simple. "Well, what do we do next?" I can hear a Mr. Kapustin asking his wife as he finishes tacking up the last holly wreath. Mrs. Kapustin peers uncertainly at her copy of *Mademoiselle.* "'Tip dips of twisted crotton sips—'" she begins. "No, wait a minute. 'Sip dips of cristed totton tips—'" Obviously, such an enterprise can only end in disaster. Either Mr. Kapustin, who is extremely short-tempered, snatches the magazine from his wife, provoking a free-for-all, or the dawn discloses two pallid house-holders on the verge of a breakdown, mumbling, "Dip, dip, dip."

Next turning his attention to the lighting, Mr. Gaba

says, "Go medieval: get Gothic-lantern effects by shielding ceiling bulbs with pierced, rectangular tin food-graters." It might be well to temper your enthusiasm for this novel hint with a pinch of caution, unless you want a dusky handmaiden mounted on a chair right in the middle of your party, grating carrots over the shoulders of your guests and murmuring bitterly to herself in Gullah. In the event you do, the best plan would be to sprinkle artificial snow around her feet and drape her with silver festoons and candy canes. It is certainly just as feasible as another of Mr. Gaba's suggestions: "Tie blown-up, red penny balloons to your outdoor Christmas trees. The kids in the block will pop them quick like a flash—but who cares?" Who indeed but an old Scrooge? I, for one, can think of no more diverting pastime than beating off stinging pellets from a bean-blower while setting 'em up in the next alley for a little marksman. The same promise of high adventure pervades still another of Mr. Gaba's proposals: "Decorate your mantel with a begged, borrowed, or stolen French horn filled cornucopia-style with holly and mistletoe." No French-horn player around Carnegie Hall will refuse to turn over his instrument to you once the purpose is explained to him. Should he prove reluctant, simply read him Mr. Gaba's article, and if that fails to stun him, sap him just below the left ear with a black-jack. Anybody so deficient in Christmas spirit, and above all a French-horn player, is hardly worth your sympathy.

Conscious of its august tradition, Vogue naturally scorns any such pinchpenny devices as the foregoing. Its article on the subject permits the reader to flatten his nose against the windows of several great houses and watch their occupants celebrate. Mrs. Fredrick Frelinghuysen, for instance, occasionally "masques all the curtains in great lengths of red mosquito netting," a mystifying rite, since there are surely no red mosquitoes in Mrs. Frelinghuysen's well-ordered home. (Who the devil Mrs. Frelinghuysen is I have no idea, but it is a cinch from the context that she has a well-ordered home.) Another family brews up an appalling mixture of port, brandy, Burgundy, almonds and raisins, called glögg, and then, I presume, proceeds to get quietly glöggy. A deeply religious bachelor, whose name is unfortunately not given, "once set his Christmas table with all sorts of mechanical toys. As the guests entered the dining room, the wound-up dolls, acrobats, animals, merry-go-rounds began performing their mechanical tricks." The effect on the guests, already reeling with glögg, must have been a curious one. Somehow, I have the feeling that everybody started turning handsprings, tearing down the smilax, and beating the tar out of the host—a thing he richly deserved.

No such chronicle, of course, would be complete without mention of Hollywood's method of observing the holiday. Mrs. Richard Barthelmess, I discovered, "often trims her trees with Cellophane tassels or opalescent glass bubbles," so refreshing after the opalescent iron bubbles one encounters everywhere. The Charles Boyers "cajole little pickaninnies to sing the Christmas carols." As one who in eight years has yet to see a pickaninny, big or little, within the confines of Beverly Hills, I can only conclude that the Boyers must range all the way to Georgia and

Mississippi for their little sable songsters. Mr. Boyer is a very persuasive article, but that threatens to stand as an all-time high in cajolery.

It was left to that ordinarily staid journal of gracious living, *House & Garden*, however, to emerge with the one truly brilliant inspiration of the season—an upsidedown evergreen tree swung from the ceiling. To any human flies within the sound of my voice, here is an open invitation: Drop around at my flat whenever you like on Christmas Eve with your suction shoes and have a cup of *glögg* on our ceiling. The Kapustins will be there and so will Mr. Gaba, if he isn't tied up (figuratively speaking, of course). You'll know me right away because my eyes will be so radiant; and, besides, I'll have a fresh mauve orchid in my hair—to say nothing of *Mademoiselle*, *Vogue* and *House & Garden*.

SMUGGLERS IN THE DUST,

or, Hollywood Hits Back

New racket, consisting of the smuggling of tourists into film studios, is being stamped out by industry execs, working in collaboration with the Better Business Bureau. Gang in downtown Los Angeles had been slipping visitors, at $7.50 per head, into the picture lots through bribery and other subterfuges.—Variety.

(Scene: A rather sordid opium den in downtown Los Angeles. Two tiers of bunks at left and right contain huddled figures, obviously slaves of the poppy. Downstage, at center, an unearthly greenish glow picks out the figure of an Old Man crouched over a kerosene lamp. He is turning an opium pill on a hat pin over the lamp flame and muttering inscrutable wisdom of the East. At left, a sliding panel in the wall, marked "Sliding Panel," and at right a telephone, unfortunately without any wires.)

OLD MAN (muttering the inscrutable wisdom of the East)—Five thousand years ago the sage hath said, "If a pepper seed takes wings, it will turn into a dragonfly, yet if a dragonfly loses its wings, it will not revert to a pepper seed." That is what the sage hath said five thousand years ago. (The door at rear opens suddenly and Bob Bundy, a young motion-picture executive, enters. He looks about curiously.)

BOB BUNDY (aside)—What a strange place! My chum Tyrone Rukeiser must have been joking when he told me to meet him here. But then, he is the smartest investigator in the Los Angeles Better Business Bureau and as bright as a new penny. With his resourcefulness and cool daring, we should soon see the last of the gang which has been slipping visitors, at $7.50 per head, into the picture lots through bribery and other subterfuges. (*Sees Old Man huddled over lamp*) Hullo! Perhaps this bit of human flotsam can assist me. . . . Have you seen a young man answering to the name of Tyrone Rukeiser?

OLD MAN (*querulously*)—No savvy Tylone Lukeiser. This No. 1 sordid hop joint, catchum plenty first-chop opium.

BOB (*aside*)—John Chinaman is a slick customer; I shall have to match wits with him. . . . Have you a telephone, my fliend?

OLD MAN—Telephone here but no wires along him.

BOB—Perhaps it will work without them. (*Into phone*) Hello, Central? Give me Tyrone Rukeiser, ace investigator of the Better Business Bureau and sworn nemesis of the gang which has been slipping visitors, at $7.50 per head, into the picture lots through bribery and other subterfuges. . . . What, he left hours ago? Oh, beans!

OLD MAN (*chuckling*)—Tylone Lukeiser allee samee big fool.

BOB (*hotly*)—Easy, Mister, easy! Anything you say about that party goes double for Bob Bundy!

OLD MAN—Bob Bundy him likewise a jerk.

BOB (*advancing with doubled fists*)—Darn your impertinence, you scum—(*Old Man rises, slips off his disguise, revealing Tyrone Rukeiser.*)

TYRONE (*good-humoredly*)—Not so fast, Bob Bundy!

172

Bob (*gasping*)—You had me nonplussed for a moment. You could pass muster anywhere, old man!

Tyrone—You bet I could pass muster [mustard]; I hate it. . . . Now look here, Bob, we have no time to lose. Have you a "roscoe" on your person?

Bob (*pats his pocket significantly*)—Yes; I brought my Mauser.

Tyrone—Good. We'll need your Mauser [mouser] for these rats.

Bob—But tell me—where are we?

Tyrone—In the stronghold of "Shameful Roger" Esterhazy, guiding genius of the gang.

Bob—Phew!

Tyrone—Exactly. And tonight finds our precious friend on the threshold of what may well be his most audacious exploit. You recall the recent disappearance of a certain Eunice Haverstraw, only daughter of wealthy Judge Haverstraw of Vandalia, Mo.?

Bob—I thought little of it at the time.

Tyrone—Few did. Through sources of information at my disposal, however, I soon found that "Shameful Roger" is keeping her prisoner in this maze of underground tunnels, employing a drug as yet little known to science, which paralyzes the will. (*Lowering his voice*) Bob, I have every reason to believe he plans to substitute her for glamorous Irene Dunne in the R.K.O. production "She Married Her Public Relations Counsel"!

Bob—The man must be a devil in human guise!

Tyrone—Furthermore, he intends to smuggle himself into Metro-Goldwyn-Mayer, pass himself off as Louis B.

Mayer, and then embark on a veritable orgy of substitution!

BOB—How to circumvent this mad enterprise calculated to strike at the very heart of the flicker industry?

TYRONE—I have been racking my pate for the solution. Luckily, I have wormed my way into the confidence of "Feathers" Blake, Esterhazy's moll, whom I am expecting here at any moment.

BOB (*soberly*)—This is playing with fire, old chap. Keep your nose clean; you are treading on dangerous ground.

TYRONE (*pushing him out the door*)—Look, you go and reconnoitre. And if you can't find Eunice Haverstraw, for God's sake dig up some new metaphors. (*As Bob exits, the sliding panel opens and "Feathers" Blake enters sinuously. She wears tight black satin and silver foxes, carries a mesh bag containing a wicked little pearl-handled revolver.*)

FEATHERS (*her eyes smoldering*)—Hello, you two-timing bastard.

TYRONE—Why, what's the matter, Feathers?

FEATHERS—Nothing. I always say that whenever I enter a room. (*Lifting her face to his*) Like me a little?

TYRONE—What do you think?

FEATHERS—What do I think?

TYRONE—Yes, what do you think?

FEATHERS—About what?

TYRONE—I forget.

FEATHERS—The trouble with you is you're more in love with love than you are with me.

TYRONE (*parrying*)—Love is a sometime thing.

FEATHERS—Well, get this, brother. You remain true to me or I'll kill you.

TYRONE (*thinking to pass it off lightly*)—You'll have to make me a better offer than that—ha-ha-ha!

FEATHERS—Quiet, you heel. (*She seals his mouth with a kiss.*)

TYRONE—I wonder if we're being quite fair to "Shameful Roger" Esterhazy.

FEATHERS—Pah! He's busy with that blonde milksop, Eunice Haverstraw.

TYRONE (*craftily*)—Where do you suppose he keeps her concealed?

FEATHERS (*off her guard*)—In a suite of apartments directly above, furnished in truly Oriental splendor.

TYRONE—Say, let's sneak up there—it might be a lark! (*A gong sounds; they turn, startled, to find "Shameful Roger" Esterhazy in the doorway. He is a sinister, well-groomed individual on the order of Cesar Romero, educated both here and abroad, speaks several languages miserably. The occupants of the bunks slide down and surround the guilty couple.*)

ESTERHAZY (*blandly*)—Good evening, my dear. . . . So you're the young man who has been meddling in my affairs. (*His men seize and bind Tyrone and Feathers.*)

TYRONE (*boldly*)—Your goose is cooked, Esterhazy. All the facts relative to your dubious operations are in a safe-deposit box at the Cordwainers' and Poulterers' National Bank—and the D.A. has the key!

ESTERHAZY—Yes, my friend, but I have you. Now, Mr. Rukeiser, we shall have a little *divertissement*, so you will please to sit very quietly in that chair. (*His aides produce a gunnysack, place Feathers inside, and open a hidden trapdoor.*)

TYRONE (*playing for time*)—You are a cunning adversary, "Shameful Roger." I confess I hardly expected to see the Los Angeles River here.

ESTERHAZY—Simply a tributary, my dear fellow, but the effect is the same. You're next, so watch closely. Lower away, lads. (*As they pick up the bag, the sharp notes of a bugle ring out offstage and eight comely misses in Girl Scout uniform burst in the door, brandishing swords made of lath. They quickly overpower Esterhazy and his confederates.*)

CORPORAL DORA AMMIDOWN (*to Tyrone*)—We got your message in the nick of time.

ESTERHAZY (*with an oath*)—Jeekers! Who are you, anyway?

THE GIRLS—The D.A.R.

ESTERHAZY—Who?

THE GIRLS—The Daughters of Albertina Rasch!

BOB BUNDY (*entering with a beautiful heiress*)—And here is Eunice Haverstraw, in fairly good condition. (*A portly gentleman in cutaway and silk hat pushes through the throng and embraces her.*)

JUDGE HAVERSTRAW (*to Tyrone*)—You've rounded up a dangerous nest of radicals, my boy. Here is my certified check for fifty thousand dollars Mex. (*His eyes twinkling*) And if Eunice still wants you—well, son, there's always a partnership open in Dostoievski, Griscom, Zarathustra & Haverstraw.

Tyrone—Thanks, Judge, but—well, I guess I have a previous commitment.

Judge Haverstraw (*loudly*)—Why, what do you mean, you insolent guttersnipe?

Tyrone (*softly, to Bob*)—Shall we tell them?

Bob (*blushing*)—If—if you like, Tyrone. (*Bob hastily removes his disguise of motion-picture executive, revealing himself to be Rosalind Russell. An instant of surprise, and then all join in a long locomotive for the lovers and troop off, leaving Feathers to kick around disconsolately in her gunnysack until the stagehands release her.*)

CURTAIN

BEAT ME, POST-IMPRESSIONIST DADDY

Any of you kids seen Somerset Maugham? I haven't run into him lately, but I'll bet those advertisements for "The Moon and Sixpence" put the roses in his cheeks. In case you've been spending the last couple of weeks underwater, the Messrs. Loew and Lewin have just transferred to the screen Mr. Maugham's novel of the ordeal of Charles Strickland, a character closely resembling Paul Gauguin. Faced with merchandising so spiritual a problem, the producers evidently recalled that Vincent van Gogh had been popularized as a man who mailed his ear to a friend, and decided to sell their boy on a similar basis. The leitmotiv of the campaign was a busty Polynesian hussy in a pitifully shrunken sarong, lolling on her back in considerable abandon and smelling a flower. Peering out of a palm tree above, mighty lak a chimp, was George Sanders in the best beard that money could buy. "I DON'T WANT LOVE! I hate it!" he was declaring petulantly. "It interferes with my work . . . and yet . . . *I'm only human!*" A second advertisement portrayed the painter in an equally disenchanted mood, over the caption "WOMEN ARE STRANGE LITTLE BEASTS! You can treat them like dogs (*he did!*)—beat them 'til your arm aches (*he did*) . . . and still they love you (*they did*). But in the end they'll get you and you are helpless in their hands."

Although Gauguin's journal, "Avant et Après," and his correspondence with D. de Montfreid are fairly blue in spots, he is not primarily remembered as passion's plaything, and these insinuations may confound the strait-laced. Now that Hollywood has thrown the ball into play, however, the following letters I recently unearthed in my bottom bureau drawer deserve careful scrutiny. They were written by the artist to my father's barber, who lived in the bureau between 1895 and 1897. Here and there I have taken the liberty of translating the rather difficult argot into current idiom, for clarity.

MATAIÉA, JULY 17, 1896

DEAR MARCUS,

Well, my old, you must think I am a fine *pascudnick* indeed not to answer you before this, but man is born to trouble as the sparks fly upward and I am winging. The day after I wrote you, who should come mousing around but that little brunette, Tia, in her loose-leaf pareu, which it's enough to melt the umber on a man's palette. It so happened I was in the hut with this tall job from Papeete, dashing off a quick pastel. I told Tia to stop needling me, but she was inconsolable. Distraught, I asked what she required. "Poi," she responded. Poi is one thing I have never refused anybody yet, Marcus, so, brushing off this other head, I made with the poi. The instant we were alone, the pretty trickster revealed her design. "I'm a strange little beast!" she cried. "Beat me 'til your arm aches!" Me, a family man. *Figurez-vous*, Marcus, what could I do? I bounced her around a bit, knocked out several of her teeth, and invited her to withdraw, as I had to complete a gouache by five o'clock. *Dame!*—the next thing I knew, Miss Goody Two-shoes had sealed the door, swallowed the key [*clef*], and I was it.

As to the painting, it goes very slowly. Kindest thanks for your new calendar, which arrived in good condition. Personally, the model is somewhat skinny for my taste and there is too much drapery, but *tiens*, that is the bourgeois style. Tell me more about that youth, the son of your patron. The boy has genius, Marcus; I have an instinct for these things. Mark me well, he will yet be another Piero della Francesca.

I pinch your claws,

PAUL

MATAIÉA, NOVEMBER 12, 1896

DEAR MARCUS,

Life here becomes increasingly tiresome, my friend; the women refuse to let me alone. How I envy Vincent those days at Arles, with nothing between him and his muse but the solar spectrum. I came to this miserable hole surfeited with civilization and its trinkets. One might as well be back in the Rue Vercingétorix. Last night I attended a native fête and, like a chump, neglected to close my door. Returning home about two with a charming person who insisted on seeing my frescoes, I found the wife of the Minister of Public Works concealed under the bed. The old story—I must beat her without further ado, treat her like a dog, else she will stop loving me. *Quelle bêtise!* My arms are so tired from flailing these cows that I can hardly mix my pigments. I sit down in a workingmen's café for an infusion; immediately I am surrounded by hordes of beauties begging me to maltreat them. I arise each morning determined to spend the day seriously. A pair of dark eyes at the window, a tender glance, and *pouf* [pouf].go my resolutions. After all, I'm only human.

I have a superb conception for a canvas which would be the very antithesis of Manet's "Olympia"—a native girl stretched on the sofa, regarding the onlooker with a mixture of fear and coquetry. At this rate I shall never finish it. Every sketch I begin ends the same. I pose the model on a divan, run my hand lightly over her back to enhance the sheen—*au fond* I am a painter of highlights—and *zut*, we are off on a tangent. For the time, merely to block in the masses, I am using a rolled-up umbrella in lieu of a girl. Actually, an ironic comment on your modern woman—all ribs and cloth. Where are those big, jolly, upholstered girls one used to see?

One fault only I find with your letters: there are too many lacunae. You say your patron's son was surprised embracing his governess. *Et alors?* What ensued? You leave too much to the imagination. Describe the scene with greater fidelity. Send photographs if possible. In any event, I must have a photo of the governess, preferably in her chemise, for a composition I am engaged on. It is an airy caprice in the manner of Watteau, quite unlike my current things—the startled governess blushing profusely, repulsing yet yielding to a diminutive satyr. I call it "Tickled Pink." Don't misunderstand, *mon copain.*

'This is simply relaxation, a change of pace from everything else I'm doing.

As ever,

PAUL

MATAIÉA, MAY 3, 1897

DEAR MARCUS,

Epochal news! I have arrived! After years of scorn and obloquy, after a lifetime of abuse from academicians and the kept press, I have at last attained official recognition! It came in the person of Mme. Dufresnoy, wife of the new Governor General, just as I was at the lowest ebb of despair. Reconstruct the scene for yourself: I was pacing moodily before my easel, alone, forgotten, attempting to wring some inspiration from the four or five scantily clad houris grouped on the dais. Suddenly, the sound of carriage wheels, and enter a vision of loveliness, a veritable Juno. What fluid rhythm, what vibrations . . . and yet a touch of that coarseness I find so piquant—I trembled like a schoolboy! But the real surprise was still to come. Housed in this ravishing exterior is no sordid Philistine but a delicate, subtle spirit attuned to mine; in a word, a connoisseur. Tales of my work have percolated through her flunkies and plenipotentiaries, and she must see it instanter. In a trice, the details are arranged—I am to bring my best canvases to the executive mansion next Tuesday for inspection. Only one cloud mars my bliss. As the house is being plastered, the view is to be held in Madame's boudoir, a pitifully small room which I fear is hardly adequate to exhibit the larger oils. Perdition! . . . but we shall make the best of it. I am in a frenzy of preparation, varnishing pictures, borrowing pomade for my hair, a hundred distractions—I must fly.

I embrace you, my dear fellow,

PAUL

P.S. One passage puzzled me in your last letter. How could your patron's son have penetrated to the landlady's room without climbing up the air-shaft? Curb his exuberance, I implore you, and do not fail to send me a snapshot of the landlady.

MATAIÉA, MAY 19, 1897

DEAR MARCUS,

My decision is irrevocable: I am through with painting. I have a new mission, the extermination of the official class and particularly of its wives. After that, the monastery.

The betrayal was complete, catastrophic. I waited on Mme. Dufresnoy afire with plans—a house in the Avenue Matignon, a summer palace on the Bosphorus, a villa at Chantilly. I am received by my benefactress in a filmy black peignoir, eyes sparkling with belladonna. The room is plunged in shadow; she prefers (sweet tyrant) to examine the canvases by artificial light. I shrug at her eccentricity, swallow a *fine à l'eau* as a digestive, launch into a short preamble about my work. *Basta!* Suddenly we are in Stygian darkness and I am held in a clasp of iron. "Madame," I entreat, "let us at least sit down and talk this thing over." *Enfin*, she reluctantly disposed herself in my lap and we had just arrived at a rationale when the door flew open and the Governor General rushed in. I could have demolished the big tub of tripes with my small finger, but he was escorted by a band of *apaches*, armed to the teeth. I acquitted myself handily, nevertheless, and outside a discolored eye and a trifling greenstick fracture, emerged an easy victor. Thanks to Madame's intercession, I was given the most spacious room in the lockup and the assignment of whitewashing the walls. It is not painting, but working with new textures is good artistic discipline.

Your letters, as always, remain my constant solace. If I may presume on our friendship, though, please to omit all further references to that miserable little brat, your patron's son. I am not interested in his grimy amours, nor anybody else's, for that matter. I have had enough of the whole god-damned subject.

Eternally,

P. Gauguin

TOMORROW — FAIRLY CLOUDY

Heaven knows I don't want to sound gossipy, but something rather important has been happening to American advertising. In fact, it almost looks as if there might be no American advertising one of these days.

Perhaps a few of you in the Older Business Boys' Division will recall an advertisement which appeared in the late twenties. It showed a well-known Russian princess clasping a Knopf book and bore the starry-eyed admission, "Mindful of my duty to the public, I am careful never to be seen without a Borzoi book." At that time I thought I heard the muffled tread of the *Jacquerie* in the streets, and I even went so far as to buy myself a pike suitable for carrying heads. I guess it was merely a case of wishful thinking. Great, fatuous booby that I was, I imagined advertising would be destroyed from the outside. It won't; it's going to bubble and heave and finally expire in the arms of two nuns, like Oscar Wilde.

The opening note of the *marche funèbre* was sounded in an advertisement for Listerine tooth paste in a recent issue of the *American Home*. It was a cartoon strip called "What Put Patty in the Movies?" and its plot was as follows: Patty, a zestful little breastful, crouches on a beach, daydreaming with her two chums. From her mouth issues a balloon with the caption, "I read somewhere there's a great call for photographers' models. Wouldn't I like to be one . . . lots of money and a chance at the movies maybe." "Why not, Patty?" urges Bob. "You'd be sure to succeed. I'll get Dad to call up his photographer friend, Mr. Hess."

In less than two panels, Mr. Hess is breaking the bad news to Patty. "I'm afraid you won't do, Miss Patty. Your teeth are good, but *not good enough*. For camera work they have to be perfect." To Miss Jones, Mr. Hess' secretary, Patty sobs out her chagrin. "I've failed, Miss Jones . . . and we needed the money so badly!" "Failed! Fiddlesticks!" counters Miss Jones briskly. "All you need to do is use a special type of tooth paste that our best models and screen stars use. LISTERINE TOOTH PASTE is its name. Try it two weeks . . . then come back."

Well, sir, you're probably psychic. "Three Weeks Later—at the Studio" introduces the fifth picture, in which Mr. Hess announces, "The job's yours, Miss Patty . . . $50 a week. I can't believe you're the same girl. Your teeth are simply perfect." "I'm so thankful, Mr. Hess," replies Patty, who is a bulldog for tenacity. "It may lead to the movies. And all the credit is due to Miss Jones." The sixth and last panel is headed "One Year Later." On the observation platform of a train, surrounded by the upturned faces of townsfolk, stands Patty, her smart tailleur festooned with orchids. "You're all so wonderful. Good-bye! Good-bye!" she calls. "She'll click in Hollywood," observes Bob stoutly to Patty's girl chum, and it is Patty's nameless girl chum whose answer should go echoing down the corridors of time. "Maybe we'd better start using LISTERINE TOOTH PASTE too," she murmurs drearily. "*Anything to get out of this hick town.*"

The italics are mine, but the desperation is that of the

186

whole advertising confraternity. So all the old tactics have finally broken down—wheedling, abuse, snobbery and terror. I look forward to the last great era in advertising, a period packed with gloom, defeatism and frustration, in which spectacles like the following will be a commonplace:

(*Scene: The combination cellar and playroom of the Bradley home in Pelham Manor. Mr. and Mrs. Bradley and their two children, Bobby and Susie, are grouped about their new automatic oil burner. They are all in faultless evening dress, including Rover, the family Airedale.*)

Bobby—Oh, Moms, I'm so glad you and Dads decided to install a Genfeedco automatic oil burner and air conditioner with the new self-ventilating screen flaps plus finger control! It is noiseless, cuts down heating bills, and makes the air we breathe richer in vita-ray particles!

Susie—Think of it! Actual experiments performed by trained engineers under filtered water prove that certain injurious poisons formerly found in cellars are actually cut down to thirty-four per cent by switching to a Genfeedco!

Mr. Bradley (*tonelessly*)—Well, I suppose anything's better than a heap of slag at this end of the cellar.

Mrs. Bradley—Yes, and thanks to Buckleboard, the new triple-ply, satin-smooth, dirt-resisting wall plastic, we now have an ugly little playroom where we can sit and loathe each other in the evening.

Bobby—Hooray for Buckleboard! Since Dads made this

feedbin into a playroom, no more hanging around the livery stable with questionable acquaintances!

MR. BRADLEY—Yes, we now have a livery stable right in our own home. The initial expense was brutal, but the money only gathered two and a half per centum in the bank.

BOBBY and SUSIE (*munching candy bars*)—Hooray! Hooray for this new taste sensation!

MRS. BRADLEY—Harvey, I'm worried about the children. Don't you think they have too much energy?

SUSIE—Choc-Nugs are just *loaded* with energy, Moms! These crackly nuggets of purest Peruvian cocoa, speckled with full-flavored, rain-washed nut meats, call forth a chorus of "Yums" from every wide-awake girl and boy!

BOBBY—In Mexico it's "Viva el Choc-Nugo!" but in America its "Hooray for Choc-Nugs!" Any way you pronounce it, it is pronounced "Goodylicious" by millions of eager candy-lovers!

MR. BRADLEY—I see that I have fathered a couple of Yahoos. . . . Bobby, answer the door.

BOBBY—Had we installed a set of Zings, the new electric chime, it would not be necessary for callers to wait outside in the rain and sleet. . . .

MR. BRADLEY—Answer the door or I will knock your block off, you murdering little saw-toothed ape. (*Bobby goes to door, admits Mr. and Mrs. Fletcher and their three children, attired in long balbriggan underwear. General greetings.*)

MRS. FLETCHER—Don't mind us, Verna, we just dropped in to sneer at your towels. (*Unfolding a towel*)

My, they're so absorbent and fluffy, aren't they? You know, they're made of selected fibres culled from high-grade flat-tailed Montana sheep subject to rigid inspection by qualified sheep inspectors.

MRS. BRADLEY (*listlessly*)—They fall apart in two days, but we got tired of using blotters.

MRS. FLETCHER—Verna, I think it's about time you and I had a heart-to-heart talk about your skin. You're as rough and scaly as an old piece of birch-bark.

MRS. BRADLEY—I know; it's my own fault. I neglected my usual beauty cocktail.

MRS. FLETCHER—Skins, you know, are divided into three types—cameo, butter-scotch, and mock nutria. Yours defies classification.

MRS. BRADLEY (*miserably*)—Oh, how can I win back my Prince Charming?

MRS. FLETCHER—Why not follow the example of glamorous Mrs. Barney Kessler, socially prominent matron of the Main Line?

MRS. BRADLEY—What does she do?

MRS. FLETCHER—Each morning, on rising, she scrubs her skin with an ordinary sink-brush. Then she gently pats in any good brand of vanishing cream until Kessler disappears to his office.

MRS. BRADLEY—And then?

MRS. FLETCHER—I can't remember, but she's got a complexion like a young girl.

MR. FLETCHER—Say, Harvey, make this test for yourself. Do some brands of pipe tobacco irritate your tongue, cause your eyeballs to capsize in your head? Then pack your old briar with velvety Pocahontas Mixture and know true smoke-ease. After all, you have to put something into your pipe. You can't just sit there like a bump on a log.

MR. BRADLEY—I get along all right smoking old leaves from my lawn.

MR. FLETCHER—Yes, but look at the fancy tin these people give you. Remember that five hundred of these tins and a fifty-word essay on "Early Kentish Brass Rubbings" entitle you to the Pocahontas Mixture vacation offer, whereby you retire at sixty with most of your faculties impaired.

MRS. FLETCHER—Er—Fred, don't you think it's time we. . . .

MR. FLETCHER—Now, Harriet, don't interrupt. Can't you see I'm talking to Harvey Bradley?

MRS. FLETCHER (timidly)—I know, but there seems to be about two feet of water in this cellar and it's rising steadily.

MR. BRADLEY (sheepishly)—I guess I should have specified Sumwenco Super-Annealed Brass Pipe throughout. My contractor warned me at the time.

MR. FLETCHER (bailing like mad with his tin)—Well, this is a pretty how-do-you-do.

MRS. BRADLEY (comfortably)—At least, whatever else happens, under the Central American Mutual Perpetual Amortizational Group Insurance Plan our loved ones need not be reduced to penury.

MRS. FLETCHER—What good is that? Our loved ones are right here with us!

Mr. Bradley (*mildly*)—You don't tell me.

Mrs. Bradley—I always say the added protection is worth the difference, don't you, Harvey? (*She pats her husband's shoulder reassuringly as they all drown like rats in a trap.*)

SWEET AND HOT

Now that Jack Frost's magic brush has made every dell a delight with delicate traceries of ice and snow, inviting each of us to turn Wandervögel and roam the woodland path with a dog in his haversack, what pulse does not quicken? My pulse, sweetie, and don't forget it. If anything, it slows down to a dead stop at the mere thought. It is on days like these that I barricade the door with my bureau, heap my stout walking shoes and parka on the coals, and settle down by the oven with a plate of cookies and the current issue of either *The Cracker Baker* or *Metronome*. Whatever energy I burn turning their pages is replaced by the cookies, which in turn are replaced by more cookies.

A pushover for crackers and sweet wafers from boyhood, I went along for years thinking I knew all there was to know about cookies. When the talk at the club turned to Fig Newtons, for instance, I could always command attention and respectful glances from the older men by describing a special kind of Fig Newton with bitter-chocolate icing I had seen. My little monograph on the mutations of Social Teas and Coffee-Mallomars had attracted a certain amount of attention, and I was preparing a definitive paper on the Butter Thin. It wasn't genius or talent, mind you; I was just better posted on the subject. You get into this little dream world of your own, and then one day, boom!. along comes *The Cracker Baker*.

Perhaps "boom!" is too strong a word to describe the

way *The Cracker Baker*, published by the American Trade Publishing Company, comes along. Maybe more of a humming or droning sound, to blend with the measured, heavy breathing of the reader as his eyes lose focus and his head droops like a sun-flower. No matter how much you adore Hydrox biscuits, it's pretty hard to take to your bosom a machine that mixes, stamps, bakes, and wraps twelve hundred of them a minute. Mother's fingers, it seems, have given way to thousands of terrifying presses which print cookies like newspapers under the most hygienic and uninteresting conditions. In this Monel-metal wilderness of cams, bushings, gears and levers, the Question-and-Answer Department of *The Cracker Baker* is a pillar of fire by day. Here the panic-stricken baker, eyes rolling and teeth chattering, blabs out his indiscretions and quivers under the lash of the editor's scorn. Less bizarre than many is the plea which appeared not long ago:

EDITOR, *The Cracker Baker:*
  We are sending you a few of our soda biscuits. As you will see they are full of fish mouths.
  Can you tell me what is the cause of that and what we could do to eliminate it.
  Thanking you, we remain,   B. C.

The editor conceals his agitation with some technical fatuities about B.C. watching his yeast. B.C. can watch his yeast from now till Christmas, but it is apparent to anybody that he is coping with nothing more or less than trolls. Somewhere along the line he has given offence to the Little People, and they have put the finger on him. I can't make out from his letter whether they are the small gnomes with the red hats and the curly shoes, or the larger, goblin type, but it is unmistakably the Good Folk at work. It was distinctly unwise of him to squeal on them to the editor of *The Cracker Baker*, but if he will leave a large crumb cake and two dozen cinnamon buns (without raisins, please) at my door every morning for a month, I shall try to intercede in his behalf.

The plight of T. B., whose chronicle was printed in a recent issue, is even more poignant:

EDITOR, *The Cracker Baker*:

I am writing you to see if you can perhaps help me. My bake shop and store is next to an automobile accessory store. Whenever the colder weather sets in these people sell a large quantity of alcohol. From handling this and carrying it through the store, the odor or smell penetrates through the walls into my store. This is very annoying and my customers ask what smells. Have you any suggestions as to what I could spray in my store that would counteract the other odor and at the same time not harm my cakes, etc. or if there is any other suggestion you can make I would be glad to hear from you.   T. B.

To suggest that T. B. spray his coffee rings and cupcakes with a scent like Arpège or Bellodgia is only to confuse him, and the expense of spraying the customers would be ruinous. Nor would it be feasible to lay down a heavy barrage of dichloroethyl sulphide or chloropicrin gas. Either of the latter would effectively counteract the alcohol, but might show a tendency to eat the features and the clothes off the customers. T. B.'s best bet is to negotiate with his fellow-craftsman, B. C., for the loan of his elves. Equipped with icing-guns and a barrel of marsh-mallow, a raiding party of these nixies might bring the accessory people to heel. If T. B. will arrange to deliver a dozen *Schnecken* and a Mocha layer cake to my home during July, I might act as liaison officer on the deal.

No matter how horrid the predicament of these unfortunate bakers, they are at ease in Zion compared to the trumpet-players whose letters stud *Metronome*, the monthly musical journal published at 113 West Fifty-seventh Street, New York City. To the column called "Trumpet Questions" come the most harrowing narratives, of which the following is a fairly typical sample:

G. S., Los Angeles, Calif., states that he has a tendency to place his trumpet at a peculiar angle to his face and wishes to know if this is wrong, and is it advisable to change the position now.

He has been playing about five years and this habit became formed within the past two years without him becoming conscious of it.

On sustained notes higher than C (middle) he is extremely nervous and his trumpet starts to shake, giving it a disagreeable wavy tone. The base of the trouble seems to be in his lips, he states. These quiver and shake, thus making the trumpet move up and down.

Unlike the bakers, G. S. forgot to enclose a sample of his face, making it almost impossible to determine whether he is placing his trumpet at a peculiar angle to it. If it is like that of most trumpet-players, however, he had better quit grumbling, as calling it a face too often will not pass unchallenged. That symptom of the lips quivering can be remedied by pasting them together; the loss to the profession would not be irreplaceable, as the medical profession can always get more paste.

In the same number of *Metronome*, W. R., of Dolgeville, N. Y., complains as follows:

> I am troubled with a lack of endurance when playing first trumpet but when playing second trumpet this does not bother me. I am playing with a ten-piece combination and have just returned from a seven-weeks' engagement, playing every night. I feel that I have had quite a bit of experience and practice during the summer to get my lip in good shape as I have been playing first trumpet in dance bands now for over a year.
>
> Does smoking injure the lip?
>
> Does playing with a dry lip make any difference in lip endurance? I use a concave rim mouthpiece and have played on that for a year. Should my lip be used to the change by now?
>
> Will you please tell me just how long it should take an average fellow of 15 to develop a strong lip?

Goodness gracious, W. R., not so fast—you'll have my head in a whirl! Now first, about smoking. Of course it won't injure your lip; that is, if you mean smoking marijuana. A man of fifteen like yourself ought to be good for his twenty or thirty a day without any harmful effect. Naturally, you may fall down once in a while, or drag your left leg slightly, but that's a detail. As for playing with a dry lip—not in public, old man. Remember, you're a big boy now. If you're really in earnest about developing a strong lip, there are a few simple rules. First, you'll have to wipe off that farina, or zwieback, or whatever that unpleasant substance is you always have on it. Then you'll have to practice hanging by your lip from branches, increasing the height every day until it becomes really dangerous. If the bough breaks, don't tighten up and get tense —just fall heavily, like a sack of meal. And finally, if you possibly can, do me one favor. Fall on your trumpet, will you? I know it's asking a lot, but it'll make me terribly happy—please.

But it is the May issue of *Metronome* which carries the report of an anonymous band leader so tragic that it lies almost too deep for tears:

This leader writes that his trumpet section is suffering from the following faults: split tones, uncertain attack, inability to hit high tones, poor vibrato, no endurance, poor phrasing, slow execution, no vibrato, and inability to read.

Even the trumpet editor, who has seen trouble as only a trumpet editor can, throws up his hands:

Evidently the most expedient way out of your difficulty is to get an entire new trumpet section.

And as for me, I'm going to get an entire new plate of cookies.

SEEDLINGS OF DESIRE

Brent Carstairs, Broadway's foremost producer, lifted a bored black eyebrow in languid amusement and bestowed a tolerant stare through sleepy eyelids on Moot Point, his general manager. His long, sensitive fingers, the fingers of a poet and dreamer he had recently acquired at auction, toyed with the skull of a soubrette which served him as a paperweight.

"This little—ah—stock actress of yours is all very well," he threw at Point, "but can't you see, Moot, the part calls for a woman of the world. . . ."

"Ach, *mein Gott!*" groaned Point in his comical German dialect, flinging his toupee on the rug and stamping on it. "He calls Gaby Papadakis a stock actress! I tell you, Brent, nefer haf I seen such youth, such fire, such . . ." Carstairs exchanged a quizzical glance with his manservant, fitted it into an ivory holder and lit it abstractedly. A muscle flickered in his lean jaw, and as its sound died out in the great room, Carstairs arose.

"All right, Moot, I'll see her," he said decisively. "Pack my bags, Eno. I'm leaving immediately for Wilkes-Barre."

"Shall I pack your flannels, sair?" queried the inscrutable Oriental.

"No, never mind them," waved Carstairs irritably. It was characteristic of the man that he usually ate a few swatches of flannel whilst traveling on trains. But today he was nervous, distraught; with the opening of *Becky's*

Blintzes scarcely a week off and no leading woman in view, he had even left a plate of tasty green billiard felt untouched at breakfast. Eno shook his head and went off muttering indignantly.

"Faix, and it's th' divil a bit he's been afther eatin'," growled Eno. "Th' loikes av thim shpalpeen play-acthors traipsin' in ivry hour av th' day an' noight a man'd gang fair daft, begorra!" And with many a rueful shake of his head, the faithful old retainer began to prepare for his master's journey.

Gaby Papadakis gave her saucy little nose an extra fillip with the powder puff and threw herself a final admiring glance in the mirror. She saw there a retroussé nose and across its bridge a dash of freckles; the next instant they were gone, without even bothering to close the door behind them. Old Pop, the stage-door watchman, beamed admiringly as she stripped off her street clothes and buckled on the Carnegie foundation which enhanced her lissom figure.

"Some feller from the city out in front tonight, Gaby," confided the old gaffer mysteriously, sucking on his cornpone with toothless gums. "Cal'late ez how yew won't be with us much longer."

"Why, Pop!" chided Gaby with a merry twinkle. "Who'd want poor little me in New York? I'd be so frightened. . . ."

"Your cue, Gaby!" She snatched up a long rope of artificial pears and strung them about her neck with a gay little laugh. Then, with pounding heart, she raced down the winding iron stairway and took her place in the wings. The opening chorus was just swelling from the orchestra:

> We greet you tonight with hearts that are light
> At the Wilkes-Barre Boat Club Show,
> We know you'll enjoy all the jokes we employ,
> For they're all quite new, you know;
> Singing, dancing, hearts entrancing,
> Fascinating, captivating boys are we, are we. . . .

From the first moment Brent Carstairs descried Gaby Papadakis he could not help placing her on a pedestal and fumigating her. Only nineteen, there was a sort of silken luster about her which fell to her knees in undulating folds. On her dainty egg-shaped head was massed a crop of auburn curls; the cucumbers she had grown there the previous summer were forgotten in the pulsing rhythm of the moment. Suffice it to say that when the curtain fell on the last act, in which Gaby went to face the firing-squad amid a fanfaronade of shoehorns, Carstairs' decision was sealed.

Then we may expect you Friday morning?" Brent Carstairs' voice was crisp as he folded the signed contract and stowed it into his plaid-back ulster.

"Y-yes," stammered Gaby. A blush mantled her cheek as the courtly impresario stooped and kissed her hand in two-four time. Long after he had gone she sat staring at his elegantly engraved card. Brent Carstairs! The name swam before her eyes. Ah, youth, youth! Canst thy bright pennons embossed with Hope's heraldry survive the blasts

of thy discontent? The words of the immortal poet Pea·
body came back to her in their full poignancy.

Gaby Papadakis stood in the swirling confusion of
Grand Central hugging her shabby portmanteau to her.
Wilkes-Barre was far behind now; she had burned her
boats, and the first step was to hunt up a doctor to pre·
scribe a soothing lotion for them. This done, Gaby re·
paired to a nearby eating-house and made a delicious
breakfast of oatcreel and meap, flanked by hot hiscuits and
bunny. Slicing down her tired feet with a steaming
draught of coffee, Gaby hurried to the offices of Brent
Carstairs. The distinguished producer looked up from
slitting his morning mail. A pleasant smile played around
the corners of his desk.

"Well, Miss Minx," he began with mock severity, "are
you ready for work—hard work? How are your muscles?"
He gave her calf a playful squeeze.

"I—I forgot to bring them along," faltered Gaby, col·
oring violently.

"You must send for them instanter," directed Car·
stairs. "We don't want any shirkers in *Beckey's Blintzes*,
Miss Papadakis. I think you had better begin your fencing
lessons immediately." He pressed one of the buttons on
his vest and "Mops," the red-headed but irrepressible
office-boy, entered.

"Take this young lady over to Beppo for a fencing les·
son," he ordered. "Oh, by the way, Miss Papadakis, have
you found quarters yet? No? Let me see—you had better
use these for the time being." He handed her a roll of
quarters and stood up. Gaby attempted to thank him, but

her fingers were all thumbs. Carstairs rubbed a blue and freshly shaven cheek against her soft one and returned it to his coat-pocket.

"Now run along to your fencing lesson, child."

All that afternoon, under Beppo's watchful supervision, Gaby learned something of the art of fencing; how to drill the holes, the proper way to string barbed wire and, finally, a few choice words to write on board fences. The next day, under the able guidance of Abel Guydens, Carstairs' dance director, she was initiated into the mysteries of Terpsichore. Each night she rubbed her aching back with Arnica, her colored maid, in close attendance. Mealtimes were spent closely scanning her lines. Every time he scanned them Brent Carstairs felt surer that he had not made a mistake. Within a week he gave up eating altogether and was spending his entire lunch hour just scanning her lines.

The opening night of *Becky's Blintzes* repaid his faith in Gaby. She was vivid, vibrant, as sure-footed as a mountain goat. All her entrances were timed to the minute, and twice when she spoke a hush fell over the house and had to be removed by the ushers. Slowly the disbelief faded from the faces of the critics and was replaced by a placidity, a tenderness so intense that it could only be called slumber. For three minutes after the curtain no sound could be heard. Carstairs, astute *entrepreneur* that he was, finally sent the stagehands through the audience beating tin pans. Then at last jaded and blasé New York first nighters were thrilled to the core. A great reverberating snore rolled like a mighty wave from the mezzanine and broke at Gaby's feet. On its surface floated odds and ends of vegetables, stewed fruit and bits of pork fat. Not since the elder Kean had Gotham seen such an ovation. Gaby, flinging her bouquet of cardiac roses to the theater-goers, kissed her hand prettily to the boxes and withdrew to the flies, who were eagerly buzzing about her in admiration. Brent Carstairs was waiting, flushed and triumphant. In vain rival producers hammered on the door with tempting contracts; red-faced advertising men, their eyes bloodshot from rich living, stormed her dressing-room with sample jars of cold cream for endorsement. But it was useless—New York's most sought-after actress had vanished into thin air.

Three miles away and four hours later, on the deck of Carstairs' private yacht, Gaby and Brent faced each other over demi-tasse. In the distance twinkled the yellow lights of Stapleton, Staten Island. At length Carstairs' voice, hoarse with passion, broke the silence.

"You remember our bargain?" he asked. There was a gleam in his small piggish eyes now which frightened her; she arose impulsively and went to the rail, drinking in the beauty of the night and attempting to marshal her thoughts. Brent's voice was at her elbow now, caressing it.

"Why do you repulse me, Gaby baby?" he begged. "You've been as cold-blooded as a fisk lately."

"Have I? Then it's time for you to retire," she told him with a light shrug. He uttered a savage laugh and attempted to sweep her into his arms. Gaby stiffened, sensing the innate brutality of the man. Brent's eyes narrowed and disappeared, but before he could make further over-ures, a pair of brawny young arms like iron pinioned his. He wheeled, his jaw dropping. A grim young face with a tangle of blond curls above it was looking into his eyes squarely.

"Oxmoor!" blenched Carstairs involuntarily.

"The same," said the young man. "You thought you'd left me behind, didn't you? You forgot that I could follow you in my amphibian." And he felled Carstairs to the deck with a single blow like an Oxmoor had felled an invading Persian at the battle of Salami three thousand years before.

"Lloyd!" What a world of relief Gaby threw into that syllabub! He took her in his arms and crushed her to him.

"I got your telephone message just in time, lover," Lloyd said huskily. "Charlotte was at Hurley's early this afternoon and found Donald. He confessed everything."

"Then you found the . . ."

"Here they are, safe and sound," he said simply, drawing the garnets from his necktie. "The detectives didn't think of looking there."

Neither of them spoke, for somehow words seemed strangely banal against the tropic beauty of the lagoon. Captain Stannard, a white patch in the darkness, coughed discreetly.

"Steam's up, sir, awaiting your orders."

"Take the wheel and relieve him, Jack." Lloyd Oxmoor's voice was gentle and almost inaudible, for his lips were grazing Gaby Papadakis's hair. "Head her toward the South Seas, Stannard; I've found heart's-ease at the end of the rainbow, old man."

KITCHENWARE, NOTIONS, LIGHTS, ACTION, CAMERA!

To the casual reader, there was nothing in yesterday's *New York Times* to distinguish it from any normal edition of that newspaper. Caught like flies in the amber of the daily screen jottings, however, were two items which easily outweighed anything on the front page. "Virginia Dale, Esther Fernandez, Dana Dale, and Martha O'Driscoll," ran the first, "have been loaned by Paramount to Harry Donahue, independent producer, to appear in a fashion short, which will be photographed in color in the Grand Canyon . . . the film will be exhibited in department stores throughout the country on a rental basis." Hard on the heels of the first came this second tidbit: "Gloria Jean, child songstress at Universal, will make a personal appearance at Gimbel Brothers at 11 A.M. today to discuss her favorite sports and life in Hollywood."

Aesthetes may decry this *rapprochement* between art and commerce, this spiritual wedding of L. B. Mayer and R. H. Macy, but I feel the match was made in heaven. The day is dawning when film and department store may fuse into a single superb medium, with mighty themes like "Resurrection" and "Gone with the Wind" harnessed directly to the task of merchandising winter sports-wear and peanut-fed hams. Once self-consciousness disappears, January white sales, midsummer clearances, and current specials will be neatly embodied in the pictures themselves, and it should surprise nobody to hear Miss

Loy address Mr. Powell thus in some future "Thin Man": "Why, hello, dear, long time no see. Yes, this divine mink coat, tailored by mink-wise craftsmen from specially selected skins, is only $578.89 at Namm's in Brooklyn, Porch & Schlagober's in Dallas, the Boston Store in Cleveland, the Cleveland Store in Boston, and Kerosene Brothers in Denver." As for the legitimate theater, it will probably preserve its usual stiff-necked attitude for a while, but in time it must adapt itself to the external pressure of pictures and radio.

As little more than a trial balloon in this direction, I append the following blueprint for a new department-store dramaturgy. In the event of a production, I suggest a week's tryout in Philadelphia, at some house like Straw-bridge & Clothier's, before bringing it into Wanamaker's or Hearns for the New York run:

Scene: The music room in the palatial villa of Mrs. Laf-cadio Mifflin at Newport. Mrs. Mifflin, a majestic woman in a slim-pin Bemberg corselet well boned over the dia-phragm (Stern Brothers, fourth floor), is seated at the console of her Wurlitzer, softly wurlitzing to herself. Mr. Mifflin, in a porous-knit union suit from Franklin Simon's street floor, is stretched out by the fire like a great, tawny cat. Inasmuch as there is a great, tawny cat stretched out alongside him, also wearing a porous-knit union suit, it is not immediately apparent which is Mifflin. Enter Celeste, a maid, in a shadow silhouette girdle and bra (Junior Misses, Lord & Taylor, fifth floor). She carries a note on a salver.

Mrs. Mifflin—Hello, Celeste. What's new in the servants' hall?

Celeste—Divil a bit. It's been sittin' on the lap av Moike, the polisman, Oi've been, bad cess to the murtherin' gossoon.

Mrs. Mifflin—Have you and Mike had words then?

Celeste—No, Oi loike the larrikin all roight, but Oi've me doubts as to his sincerity. Oi suspect the craythur av havin' a woife and two childer, alanna.

Mrs. Mifflin—Then brush him off, lest you become involved in a bigamous action. (*Taking the note*) My, what attractive stationery! Eaton, Crane & Pike (Bloomingdale's mezzanine), isn't it?

Celeste (*coarsely*)—It ain't Eaton, Crane & Pike's brother.

Mrs. Mifflin—That will do, Celeste. I obscenity in the obscenity of your obscenity. (*Celeste goes, Mrs. Mifflin opens note.*) Oh, how provoking!

Mifflin—What's the matter, dear?

Mrs. Mifflin—Our big gray gelding kicked one of the grooms in a fit of temper.

Mifflin—Better sell the brute. He hurt two stableboys last week.

Mrs. Mifflin—No, that was a horse of a different choler. (*Thoughtfully*) Martin, I'm worried.

Mifflin—What about?

Mrs. Mifflin—Our daughter Gisèle, yclept Tucky. As you know, she has conceived an unfortunate attachment for a barber. Inquiries I have caused to be made reveal the man to be little better than a fortune-hunter.

MIFFLIN—This is alarming news. As you know, her engagement to Stacy Bonbright IV was a foregone conclusion.

MRS. MIFFLIN—You mean the brilliant young aviator and six-goal man whose athaletic career at Bowdoin and subsequent speculations in Wall Street have made him the catch of the season?

MIFFLIN—The same.

MRS. MIFFLIN—Martin, this tawdry infatuation with a barber must be terminated.

MIFFLIN—How did she first meet this—this person?

MRS. MIFFLIN—It was a typical Tucky Mifflin escapade. Headstrong child that she is, she refused to have her hair washed in any one of several department-store salons where courteous attendants and sympathetic service insure satisfaction. Instead, she visited an establishment upstairs over a poolroom and encountered the coiffeur in question.

MIFFLIN—How to resolve this perplexing state of affairs?

MRS. MIFFLIN—I have a plan. Why not consult our favorite department store? As you know, nationwide credit facilities maintain a close surveillance on the character and reliability of customers. Should this Luigi, as he styles himself, have come under their scrutiny—

MIFFLIN—Capital. (*He picks up a tomato can connected by a length of waxed string with New York.*) Hello, Central, give me the credit bureau of my favorite department store. . . . Hello? This is Martin Mifflin.

What information have you on a party named Luigi?
... Yes? ... Yes ... Indeed. Thank you.

Mrs. Mifflin (anxiously)—Were our apprehensions justified?

Mifflin—Fully. This scalawag who has led Gisèle down the garden path is none other than Mike, the quondam policeman currently laying siege to Celeste. As she feared, the rogue has a wife and two children. But thanks to the watchdog who never sleeps (organized retail credit investigation), our child is safe. (*The door opens and Gisèle bursts in, accompanied by Stacy Bonbright IV.*)

Gisele—Oh, Mother, what a little goose you must think me! Fortunately, I discovered my error in time and married Stacy Bonbright IV.

Mifflin—Take her, my boy. You've earned her, as well as this sight draft for several million dollars.

Stacy (*warmly*)—Thanks, sport.

Gisele—How do you like my wedding tailleur, Mother?

Mrs. Mifflin—It's a heller. Altman's, of course?

Gisele—Yes, and available in nineteen different shades —among them wine, russet, beige, peach, grackle, stone liver, lover, blubber, blabber and clabber.

Mifflin—And now, children, what are your honeymoon plans? Hot Springs, Placid? Sun Valley?

Gisele (*dimpling*)—Not on your tintype, Father. Just plain, old-fashioned Saks.

CURTAIN

CAPTAIN FUTURE, BLOCK THAT KICK!

I guess I'm just an old mad scientist at bottom. Give me an underground laboratory, half a dozen atom-smashers, and a beautiful girl in a diaphanous veil waiting to be turned into a chimpanzee, and I care not who writes the nation's laws. You'll have to leave my meals on a tray outside the door because I'll be working pretty late on the secret of making myself invisible, which may take me almost until eleven o'clock. Oh, yes, and don't let's forget one more thing. I'll need a life subscription to a new quarterly journal called *Captain Future, Wizard of Science*, a bright diadem on the forehead of Better Publications, 22 West Forty-eighth Street, New York City.

As one who triggered a disintegrator with Buck Rogers and could dash off a topographical map of Mongo or Dale Arden with equal facility, I thought in my pride and arrogance I knew all there was to know about astronomical adventure. It was something of a shock, therefore, to find out several days back that I was little more than a slippered pantaloon. Beside Captain Future, Wizard of Science, Flash Gordon and the Emperor Ming pale to a couple of nursery tots chewing on Holland rusk.

The novelette in which this spectacular *caballero* makes his bow to "scientification" fans opens with no fumbling preamble or prosy exposition. Into the office of James Carthew, President of the Earth Government, staggers a giant ape, barely recognizable by the President as John Sperling, his most trusted secret agent. The luckless investigator had been ordered to Jupiter to look into a complaint that some merry-andrew was causing atavism among the Jovians, but apparently had got badly jobbed. Before Carthew can intervene, a frightened guard drills the ape man with a flare-pistol, and in his dying breath the latter lays the blame for his predicament squarely at the door of a mysterious being he calls the Space Emperor. As you may well imagine, Carthew is all of a tizzy. He immediately instructs his secretary to send for Captain Future in the ringing phrase, "Televise the meteorological rocket-patrol base at Spitzbergen. Order them to flash the magnesium flare signal from the North Pole." Personally, I think Carthew might have softened this whiplike command with "And just for the hell of it, why don't you try the Princeton Club?" but perhaps I delve too deeply. In any event, the perpetual uranium clock has hardly ticked off two hours before Captain Future (or Curt Newton, to call him by his given name) appears on the escarpment with one of the most endearing speeches in my experience:

"You know my assistants," Curt Newton said shortly, "Crag the robot, Otho the android, and Simon Wright, the Living Brain. We came from the moon full speed when I saw your signal. What's wrong?"

Fiction teems with sinister escorts and everybody has his favorite, but Captain Future's three-man mob leaves the worst of them kissed off and frozen against the cushion:

A weird shape had just leaped onto the balcony. It was a manlike figure, but one whose body was rubbery, boneless-looking, blank-white in color. He wore a metal harness, and his long, slitted green unhuman eyes peered brightly out of an alien white face. Following this rubbery android, or synthetic man, came another figure, equally as strange—a giant metal robot who strode across the balcony on padded feet. He towered seven feet high. In his bulbous metal head gleamed a pair of photoelectric eyes. The robot's left hand carried the handle of a square transparent box. Inside it a living brain was housed. In the front of the case were the Brain's two glittering glass lens-eyes. Even now they were moving on their flexible metal stalks to look at the President.

At this juncture I took time out to moisten my lips with the tip of my tongue, retrieved my own eyeballs, and plunged on. Captain Future himself was somewhat more tailored than his comrades, in fact quite swagger. "His unruly shock of red hair towercd six feet four above the floor, and his wide lithe shoulders threatened to burst the jacket of his gray synthesilk zipper-suit." In pulp fiction it is a rigid convention that the hero's shoulders and the heroine's balcon constantly threatens to burst their bonds, a possibility which keeps the audience in a state of tense expectancy. Unfortunately for the fans, however, recent tests reveal that the wisp of chiffon which stands between the publisher and the postal laws has the tensile strength of drop-forged steel.

To acquaint the reader more fully with "that tall, cheer-ful, red-haired young adventurer of the ready laugh and flying fists, the implacable Nemesis of all oppressors and exploiters of the System's human and planetary races," the author interrupts his smoking narrative with a brief dossier. In the year 1990, the brilliant young Earth biologist Roger Newton, aided by the living brain of Simon Wright ("the greatest brain in scientific history"), had unravelled the secret of artificial life. Now, certain dark forces headed by one Victor Corvo were determined to appropriate Newton's secret. To confound him, Roger Newton proposed to Elaine, his wife, and the Living Brain that they conceal themselves on the moon.

"But the moon!" Elaine exclaimed, deep repulsion shadowing her eyes. "That barren, airless globe that no one ever visits!" Elaine's dainty disgust is pardonable; Far Rockaway out of season could not have been more painfully *vieux jeu*. A few weeks, nevertheless, see the little company snugly housed under the surface of Tycho crater upon the moon, where its number is swelled by the addition of the infant Curt and Grag the robot, whom Roger and the Living Brain construct in their spare time of neurons and nails and puppy dogs' tails. Eventually, still another fruit of this intellectual union—Otho, the synthetic android—is capering about the laboratory. Just as Newton is on the verge of returning to earth, up turns Public Bad Penny No. 1, Victor Corvo, and slays him and his wife. When the Brain assures him vengeance will be swift, Corvo hurls the taunt supreme at the preserved scientist: "Don't try to threaten me, you miserable bodiless brain! I'll soon silence you—" He stops throwing his weight around soon enough when Grag and Otho burst in, and, directed by the Brain, rub him out effectively if none too tidily.

213

Dying, Elaine Newton entrusts Curt to the care of the trio in a scene which must affect the sensibilities of the most callous:

"Tell him to war always against those who would pervert science to sinister ambition," whispered Elaine. "I will tell him," promised the Brain, and in its toneless metallic voice was a queer catch.

The guardians justify Elaine's faith in them to a degree; by the time Curt has attained his majority, he is one lovely hunk of boy, a hybrid of Leonardo da Vinci and Dink Stover. From then on, as Captain Future, Curt ranges the solar system with his pals in an asteroidal supership, the Comet, avenging his folks and relentlessly waging war on what the author is pleased to call "interplanetary crime."

But to return to our muttons, if so prosaic a term can be applied to the streamlined quartet. Speeding outward into space toward Jovopolis, chief Earthman colony on Jupiter, Captain Future plucks haunting music from his twenty-string Venusian guitar while Grag and Otho tend the controls and the Living Brain burrows into textbooks for a clue to the atavism. Their snug Kaffeeklatsch is blasted when a piratical black space-cruiser suddenly looms across the Comet's bows and attempts to ambush the party, but Curt's proton beams force the attacker down on Callisto, outermost of Jupiter's four biggest moons. The boys warp in alongside and Grag prepares to rip open the jammed door of the pirate craft so his master may question the miscreants:

Grag's big metal fingers were removable. The robot rapidly unscrewed two of them and replaced them with small drills which he took from a kit of scalpels, chisels, and similar tools carried in a little locker in his metal side. Then Grag touched a switch on his wrist. The two drills which had replaced two of his fingers whirled hummingly. He quickly used them to drill six holes in the edge of the ship's door. Then he replaced the drills with his fingers, hooked six fingers inside the holes he had made.

The rest is brute strength, a department in which Grag is pre-eminent. Inside are Jon Orris and Martin Skeel, whose names instantly tip them off as wrong guys. Yet it is impossible not to be moved by Orris's pathetic confession: "Skeel and I have criminal records. We fled out here after we got into a murder scrape on Mars." They admit under pressure that they are creatures of the Space Emperor, though actually they have never seen him. "He's always concealed in a big, queer black suit, and he speaks out of it in a voice that don't sound human to me," Skeel says.

Time, even on Callisto, is a-wastin', and nimbly dodging a plague of creeping crystals which bids fair to annihilate them, the space-farers resume their course. On their arrival at Jovopolis, Otho the android disguises himself as Orris and repairs to that worthy's hut to await the Space Emperor and overpower him so that Captain Future can steal up and clap the darbies on him. Arriving at the rendezvous, the Emperor promptly makes himself invisible and Curt leaps through him, only to sprawl on his finely chiseled beezer.

Recovering from this contretemps with his usual sunny equanimity, Curt hastens to the mansion of the governor, Sylvanus Quale, to reconnoitre. Here he encounters the heart interest, a plump little cabbage named Joan Randall, who is head nurse to the chief planetary physician. Lucas Brewer, a shifty radium magnate, Mark Cannig, his mine superintendent, and Eldred Kells, the vice-governor, are also at the mansion. It is apparent at once to the cognoscenti that any one of these worthies is the Space Emperor, and with no personal bias other than that his name had a particularly sneaky sound, I put my money on Eldred Kells. Fifty pages later I was proved right, but not before I had been locked in an atavism ward with Curt and Joan, flung into a pit by the green flippermen, and nibbled by giant six-foot rats called "diggers" (a surprisingly mild name for a giant six-foot rat, by the way). But even such hazards, for all their jewelled prose, cannot compare with the description of the main street of Jungletown:

Here were husky prospectors in stained zipper-suits, furtive, unshaven space-bums begging, cool-eyed interplanetary gamblers, gaunt engineers in high boots with flare-pistols at their belts, bronzed space-sailors up from Jovopolis for a carousal in the wildest new frontier-town in the System.

And so, all too soon for both Joan Randall and myself, comes the hour of parting with "the big red-head," as the author shakily describes Curt in a final burst of emotion. In the next issue, Captain Future and his creepy constabulary will doubtless be summoned forth again to combat some horror as yet to be devised. Meanwhile I like to think of his lighthearted rebuke to Otho the android, already chafing against inactivity:

"Sooner or later, there'll be another call from Earth, and then I hope there's action enough for you, you crazy coot."

There may be another call, Curt, but it won't come from Baby. Right now all he wants is a cup of hot milk and fourteen hours of shut-eye. And if it's all the same to you, he'll do his sleeping with the lights on.

ADORABLE, TAXABLE YOU

Lord love you, child, I am only a lantern-jawed individual with progressive myopia caused by attempting to cope with the current literary output, and I certainly don't want to usurp any reviewer's job in the Sunday book section. But when I see an authentic human document go begging while Messrs. Duffus, Adams and Jack whoop up the latest trilogy, I could spit. . . . Now, listen to me, Vardis Fisher and Jules Romains, you stop sulking in that corner. This is the last time Nanny ever takes you to a party.

If "Income Tax," by David Joseph, C.P.A. (Authentic Publications Co., New York, twenty-five cents), has received less than critical acclaim, its fate at the hands of the consumer is much more gratifying. It was selling like hot cakes the day I got my copy at a cut-rate drugstore; in fact, a stack of hot cakes nearby was entirely ignored and fast becoming cold cakes while customers fought with each other around a dwindling pile of Mr. Joseph's "Income Tax." In a speculation worthy of Daniel Drew, I finally secured one from an elderly party in bombazine by trading a two-volume "History of Flagellation" and half a chocolate malted. I still think I came off top dog, and the feeling must have been wide-spread, for on learning of the incident, the eminent bibliophile Dr. A. S. W. Rosenbach declared, "He came off top dog."

It is well to be forewarned that the general effect of "Income Tax" is closely akin to that of inhaling dental gas, unless you are the sort to whom tax-free covenant bonds, fiduciaries, and Canal Zone retirement funds are meat and drink. Only when Mr. Joseph turns to his files for actual visual examples—case histories, so to speak—does his book come alive, and then with a vigor and bounce unmatched in Freud. And as if the lives of James Taxpayer and John and Frances Wedd were not vivid enough already, the author presents them in facsimile income-tax returns, a device any novelist would have given his Windsor tie to anticipate.

Form 1040 A, a year in the life of James Taxpayer, finds him living quietly in the Bronx, working as pianist in a band—whether sweet, boogie-woogie, New Orleans, or Chicago style the return neglects to set forth. Judging from his somewhat colorless name, however, and the twenty-six dollars he contributed to "Non-sectarian Church," I see James as a sallow young man given to lush interpretations of "Beautiful Ohio," with pianola effects in the manner of Adam Carroll. The band is clearly a five-piece combination whose members put on funny hats about nine-thirty, and James, for his specialty, plays "Margie" as it might be done by a Swede, a Chinese, and so forth.

All in all, a respectable if prosaic citizen—until you begin analyzing his income and deductions. Then you discover from Schedule A that James received $2,600 in 1940 from something called Dance Corp., at 1463 East Eleventh Street, New York City. The firm is undeniably solvent; completely so, since it appears to be doing business in thirty-two feet of water in the middle of the East River. The pattern becomes even more complex with the deduction of $40 for "cost of substitute in band." Appraising James' services at five dollars an evening (probably much too high), it is obvious he was missing from the aggregation eight times during the past year. Drunk? Possibly. Muggled up, more than likely—an impression irresistibly borne out by the deductions in Schedule F: "Portfolio stolen, $35" and "Fire loss (not covered by insurance), $112." Quite patiently, James had been smoking a stick of tea in some rib joint and in a burst of generosity presented a total stranger with his portfolio, which was full of piano scores. After which he promptly went home and set fire to his bed, if not his mother. A bad lot, you may depend on it, and a constant source of aggravation to some lovely old white-haired booking agent.

The joint return filed by John and Frances Wedd also reveals an existence at once humdrum and bizarre. The income of this apparently irreproachable pair was derived from a variety of sources: John's salary as a teacher, a snug little annuity, several hundred shares of stock, and oddly enough, a matter of $9,994.92 rising out of a business known as Importers & Exporters, located at 2 Export Street, New York. It would seem from this hasty survey that John is that rare amalgam of dreamy pedagogue and ruthless business man in whose company it is advisable to keep your wallet pinned inside your shirt. The nature of the business transacted by John's firm is fairly obscure. For a while I thought he might be selling silver foxes from unmarked trucks, but sober reflection and a naturally sensual bias convinced me that he is engaged in what the League of Nations Committee euphemistically refers to as the South American export trade. The concept of a school teacher exporting comely lassies to Buenos Aires is undeniably romantic, but what is meant by the deduction on Line 6 of Schedule D, "Clearances, Charges and Garbage, $7,417.21?" It seems unfair. I, who lead a much more upright life than John, have never been allowed any substantial deduction for garbage, and even if the word should have been "cartage," that hardly alters the case. Whatever expenses John incurs in moving his young wards are normal overhead and definitely a part of the taxable total. Not a very good example to set our Latin neighbors, John, you dirty chiseler, you.

I expect to be accused of distortion and formulating too-facile moral judgments, but the financial complexities of the Wedds are as nothing compared to their home life. Behind a façade of bourgeois domesticity there was enacted in 1940 as feverish a scene as any Alfred Hitchcock ever directed. For in that year the Wedds were domiciled at 1 Sunset Park, in Brooklyn, sharing their brick two-family house with a tenant who paid them $900 in rent. The detail is insignificant until, in Schedule C, you encounter the chilling deduction "Painting and decorating tenant, $75." Extraordinary things have been known to take place in Brooklyn, as witness "Arsenic and Old Lace," but I submit that Mr. Karloff must bend the knee to John and Frances Wedd. It needs no lurid imagination to envision the tableau: the tenant, powerless under the influence of a mysterious drug prepared in a basement laboratory by John Wedd; laughing Frances and more serious-minded John fussing over their color cards, she, with her woman's instinct for gay plumage, trying to per suade her husband to stipple the tenant twilight blue; and, merely as an accent in the darkened room, the tenant's eyeballs gleaming whitely in his head. . . .

This is presumably Mr. Joseph's first book, and if he has his faults, so did Poe and Henry James. His prose is childish, his grammar unspeakable, and his point of view materialistic, but I loved every word, even the ones that made me sleepy. Here is a book for youngsters from nine to ninety, for anybody who likes to hold on to his money. It is dedicated, says a simple foreword, "to the purpose of giving the public what it needs—when it needs it—in the form in which it needs it—and at a price which all can afford." And with French vermouth and nose candy selling at their current quotations, Mr. Joseph, you've got the only game in town.

A COUPLE OF QUICK ONES

Two Portraits

I. ARTHUR KOBER

Picture to yourself a ruddy-cheeked, stocky sort of chap, dressed in loose but smelly tweeds, a stubby briar between his teeth (it has resisted the efforts of the best surgeons to extract it), with a firm yet humorous mouth, generous to a fault, ever-ready for a flagon of nut-brown ale with his cronies, possessing the courage of a lion, the tenderness of a Florence Nightingale, and the conceit of a diva, an intellectual vagabond, a connoisseur of first editions, fine vintages, and beautiful women, well above six feet in height and distinguished for his pallor, a dweller in the world of books, his keen gray eye belying the sensual lip beneath, equally at home browsing through the bookstalls along Fourth Avenue and rubbing elbows (his own elbows) in the smart literary salons of 57th Street, a rigid abstainer and non-smoker who lives entirely on dehydrated fruits, cereals, and nuts, rarely leaving his monastic cell nowadays except to dine at the Salmagundi; an intimate of Cocteau, Picasso, Joyce and Lincoln Kirstein, a dead shot, a past master of the foils and the International Woodmen of the World, dictating his novels, plays, poems, short stories, *commedias dell' arte*, aphorisms, and ripostes at lightning speed to a staff of underpaid secretaries, an expert judge of horseflesh, the owner of a model farm equipped with the most slovenly dairy devices—a man as sharp as a razor, as dull as a hoe, as clean as a whistle, as tough as nails, as white as snow, as black as the raven's wing, as poor as Job, a man up with the lark, down on your toes, and gone with the wind. A man kind and captious, sweet and sour, fat and thin, tall and short, racked with fever, plagued by the locust, beset by witches, hagridden, cross-grained, fancy-free, a funloving, addle-pated dreamer, visionary, and slippered pantaloon. Picture to yourself such a man, I say, and you won't have the faintest conception of Arthur Kober.

To begin with, the author of *Having Wonderful Time*, *My Dear Bella* and *Thunder Over the Bronx*, is only eighteen inches high. He is very sensitive about his stature and goes out only after dark, and then armed with a tiny umbrella with which he beats off cats who try to attack him. Not that he is antipathetic to cats; far from it. He loves tabbies of all kinds and has done everything to encourage a reciprocal feeling in them, even going so far as to roll in catnip nightly, but there is something about Kober that just makes cats' nerves tingle. Since he is unable to climb into his bed, which is at least two feet taller than himself, he has been forced to sleep in the lowest drawer of a bureau since childhood, and is somewhat savage as a result. He is meticulously dressed, however, and never goes abroad without his green cloth gloves and neat nankeen breeches.

His age is a matter of speculation. He claims to remember the Battle of the Boyne and on a fine night his piping may be heard in the glen, his voice lifted in the strains of *For She's My Molly-O*. Of one thing we can be sure; he was seen by unimpeachable witnesses at Austerlitz, Jena, and Wagram, where he made personal appearances through the courtesy of his agent, Milton Fink of the Fink and Biesmyer office. It is also fairly certain that he first conceived the idea of naming blucher shoes in honor of the gruff Marshal after Waterloo. That he invented the Welsbach mantle is not only improbable but downright foolish. The Welsbach mantle was invented by Teddy Welsbach, and there are plenty of the old Chalkstone Avenue gang left to prove it.

What I like most about Kober is his mouth, a jagged magenta wound etched against the unforgettable blankness of his face. It is a bright flag of surrender, a dental challenge. I love his sudden impish smile, the twinkle of his alert green eyes, and the print of his cloven foot in the shrubbery. I love the curly brown locks cascading down his receding forehead; I love the Mendelian characteristics he has inherited from his father Mendel; I love the wind in the willows, the boy in the bush, and the Seven against Thebes. I love coffee, I love tea, I love the girls, and the girls love me. And I'm going to be a civil engineer when I grow up, no matter what Mamma says.

At first blush one is inclined to wonder at the wedding of this strange talent with that of Marc Connelly, whose production and direction of *Having Wonderful Time* made his name a household word from McKeesport, Pennsylvania, to the Shanghai Bund. Connelly, the gruff, brown-faced old salt who served under Teach, Lafitte, Flint (ay, Flint, there was the flower of the flock, was Flint) and every notable buccaneer who ever careened his rakish black craft along the Caribbean; Connelly, known aboard all the pearling luggers out of Thursday Island with a cargo of shell; Connelly, the mere mention of whom would strike terror into the denizens of boozing-kens in Paramaribo and shebeens in Belfast; Connelly, with his black varnished straw hat and parrot on his shoulder, ready to swarm up the mizzen at the first shrill of the bos'n's fife; a powder-monkey under Nelson, gunners' mate under Klaw and Erlanger, and supercargo under the Shuberts. Lingering over your gin *pahit* on the porch of Shepheard's Hotel in Cairo, you will be told that if you remain there long enough Willie Maugham, Marc Connelly, and little black specks will pass before your eyes. It is no idle boast.

How, then, did Arthur Kober and Marc Connelly meet and conceive the idea of *Having Wonderful Time?* You must see in your mind's eye a tiny village in the Swiss Alps. The tinkle of bells in the distance heralds a herd of grazing cows and promises innumerable cakes of Peter's Milk Chocolate; nearby a smiling peasant who looks like the tyrant Gessler shucks almonds for the toothsome candy-bars. Across yonder snow-capped peaks Hannibal led his swaying elephants into Cisalpine Gaul. The station platform, deserted until now, suddenly becomes the scene of an altercation. At the railway bookstall, Kober, dressed in his favorite costume, a gunny sack and a pair of Thom McAn shoes, is glaring at the attendant, who has just accused him of stealing a banana. Kober's Italian is imperfect, his French is as faulty as his German, and his English is no bargain either. Haltingly he begins to explain to the attendant that he is innocent and that what is happening to him shouldn't happen to a Schnauzer. Unbeknownst to both, a dusty and middle-aged gentleman has moved a bit closer. He looks very much like the Father Brown of the immortal detective stories except that he is not dressed as a priest and he has absolutely no talent as a sleuth. This is Marc Connelly, fresh from a holiday in Paris; even now, unknown to the French Sûreté, the famous painting of Mona Lisa is wrapped around his body. Immediately a tensity is felt on the platform, and its sole other occupant, a St. Bernard dog, resumes scratching its fleas. A few quiet words spoken out of the side of Connelly's mouth, Kober returns the banana, and the two men fall into conversation.

Over a table in a quiet *bierstube*, Connelly learns with some surprise that Kober has written a play. Connelly, in his spare time the author of *The Wisdom Tooth*, the co-author of *Beggar on Horseback*, *Dulcy*, *To the Ladies*, and *The Farmer Takes a Wife*, his ears still pink from the plaudits he earned from *The Green Pastures*, looks at the youth with interest. Has Kober the play with him? The words have barely escaped him before the young man whips open his satchel and is thumbing the pages of *Having Wonderful Time*, chuckling over the jokes, guffawing over the stage directions, and generally giving the waiters the horrors. Connelly, recalling the incident, winces, "Frankly, I was nonplussed. The color drained away from beneath my ordinarily healthy tan and was replaced by a greenish mixture composed of 2 gr. sodium Amytal, .005 spirits of benzoin, and a cup of farina. I realized that I would have to quiet this extraordinary individual, even at the cost of producing his play." And before he knew it, Connelly, who hates a scene, had secured a signature on a minimum basic contract from Kober, who loves a scene. The effect was more soothing than even Connelly had dreamed. At once fun and jollity reigned supreme. Kober strummed a lively air on his balalaika, cocoa and "hot wieners" were the order of the day, and Connelly, always irrepressible, found a false nose in his luggage and gave an imitation of Jimmy Durante. Not to be outdone, Jimmy Durante, who had just stepped off the Orient Express, found a false nose and gave an imitation of Marc Connelly. And late that night the deal was consummated on the exchange of five hundred Confederate dollars, which the pair jokingly pretended was real currency.

Such was their buoyancy that it was first proposed to limit admission to *Having Wonderful Time* to ten pins or whatever vegetables the patrons could muckle from their parents' kitchens; but on reconsideration Connelly decided that it would only confuse the ticket speculators, and they might as well adhere to the customary toll charges. With this point of view Kober quickly fell in; Connelly tumbled in beside him, and soon the twain, deep in their feather bed, were snoring away as pleasant as you please.

Rehearsals of the play were unique in theatrical annals in several respects. When Marc Connelly is directing, he insists that all the seats be removed from the theatre and be replaced by horsehair lounges. "The Romans," he argues, "reclined at table—Petronius will vouch for that, as well as some other pretty interesting things. Why not recline at the theater? You say the audience will not accept the idea?" Here he gives a typically Gallic shrug of the shoulders and smiles disarmingly. "There are more ways to catch a finch than by putting salt on its tail." As a result, *Having Wonderful Time* offered an additional service to playgoers. Between the acts, hundreds of finches were released in the smoking lounge and the customers were shown numerous ingenious ways of catching them. When I pointed out to Kober the fact that this bore no direct connection with his play, a picture of life in a summer camp, he gave me a typically Gallic shrug of the shoulders. "After all," he observed, trimming a goose-quill with which to tickle the leading lady, "you can't give them *everything*. We don't pretend we're 'Chu Chin Chow.' " And he accepted a pinch from my snuff-box and sprinkled it on the tail of a passing finch with a cavalier gesture.

"Pictures?" replied both Connelly and Kober, when I asked them about the future of films, a medium which both have studied at close range. "We don't think so. You'll never get people into those drafty darkened stores to look at images flickering over a sheet. You see, *mon vieux*, it's artificial. Oh yes, we've heard that a man's produced *The Great K. & A. Train Robbery*, but it'll never catch on. Passing fad and all that sort of thing, you know. Give us the theater every time. And another thing." I waited attentively, my pencil poised. "Didn't we tell you to get the hell out of this theater a half an hour ago?"

They accompanied me as far as the door, their hands resting paternally on my shoulder and collar lest I wriggle free of their grasp. I recovered my footing and dusted myself, having inadvertently tripped over a jardinière crossing the lobby. Already the lights were soft moons in the streets. I turned back to look at them as they stood framed against the ticket window, the bulbs on the marquee winking Having Wonderful Time as energetically as if the current had been paid for. They held up their hands, shaking their fists playfully at me in farewell. With a tug at my heart and an extra one at my trousers, I crept down Forty-fifth Street, munching an apple I had stolen from a fruit vendor, and pondering the mystery and the glamor of the theater.

2. VINCENTE MINNELLI

One sweltering summer's day a dozen years ago I had dropped into the main reading-room of the New York Public Library. I was deep in Bulfinch's Age of Fable, busily shading the illustrations of Greek and Roman divinities with a hard pencil and getting some truly splendid effects, when I became aware that a strange individual had entered the room. He was apparently a foreigner, for he bore in his lapel a green immigrant tag reading "Ellis Island—Rush." His clothes were flapping hand-me-downs greasy with travel, and altogether, he was as extraordinary an unhung horse-thief as you would encounter outside a gypsy encampment. Before him this fantastic creature propelled an ancient hurdy-gurdy, and as he ground out a wheezy catchpenny tune, made a rapid circuit of the tables, offering highest cash prices for old bones, rubber, bottles, and newspapers. Failing to stir up any interest among the few high-school boys furtively hunting for dirty words in the dictionary, this bird of ill-omen managed to secrete a set of Ridpath's *History of the World* under his rusty caftan and disappeared, obviously to rifle the coatroom. The languid librarian to whom I addressed my query contented himself with a curt "Vincente Minnelli" and resumed buffing his nails.

I had forgotten his rapacious face when one morning several weeks later he fell into step with me on Forty-fifth Street. He proposed to sell me a set of amusing postcards and a recondite pamphlet called *The Enigmatic Miss Floggy*, but when he suggested that I follow him into an alley for an inspection of these wares, I refused shortly. With no resentment, he offered me a deck of cocaine for fifty cents. I crossed the street hoping to shake him off, but he clung like a leech. Through his connections in the "milieu" he could obtain young virgins for a hundred and fifty dollars. Screaming, I fled into a cab, only to discover that he had purloined my watch-fob, a cheap German silver affair I had won in a debating contest. Outside of the sick headache I experienced, I found that I had contracted no diseases from the encounter.

I saw him occasionally in the months that followed, sometimes as a pitchman hawking mending-cement and verses of popular songs, again as a steerer for floating crap games. For a time he ran a trap-line of telephone booths, stuffing the slots and calling for the accumulated nickels each evening. Now and then he rolled a lush. His fear of risking his cowardly hide naturally kept him from participating in a really dangerous caper.

In time I began to feel a curious affection for this cheerful vagabond, possibly because he had never drawn a knife on me. After the six months he spent in the workhouse for suspected arson, I was almost glad to see him again. To my surprise I found that he had gone into a new business. Somewhere he had picked up the stub of a pencil and a square of Bristol board. The ultimate result, some years later, was a show called *Life Begins* at 8:40.

The police *dossier* on this curious starveling is limited unfortunately to the record of several shabby misdemeanors, such as his pathetic attempt to palm off a papier-mâché goose on a poultryman. This exploit would never have entangled him with the law had it not been for a remark of the poultryman. "D'ye see any green in my eye?" he demanded scornfully, flinging the goose at Minnelli's head. "Yes," replied the culprit truthfully, for it so happened that Minnelli, whose color sense even then was unerring, detected green in his eye. The ensuing fracas saw several pates broken under the quarterstaff of the churlish poultryman, and Minnelli was dragged off ingloriously to be booked. It is almost unnecessary to note that he made his escape from prison by his usual method of having a rope pie smuggled in to him.

That I should have mistaken him for a foreigner on first seeing him is hard to reconcile with the fact that he is a Middle-Westerner and had never been east of Chicago (or worn shoes, for that matter) up to his arrival in New York in 1928. His love for bizarre dress is a byword. Even today, with any number of Broadway shows behind him, he is spending next year's royalties on flowered surtouts and sword canes. It is nothing to see Minnelli parading down Broadway of an afternoon dressed as Cameo Kirby, complete with silk tile, ruffles at his wrists, and derringer up his sleeve. That surly ruffian in black neckcloth with the craven dog at his heels who rudely elbows you aside as you enter Lindy's is less apt to be Bill Sykes than Vincente Minnelli, about to commit mayhem on a Maatjes herring.

The biographer of his early years is hard put to sift fact from legend. He was born in Delaware, Ohio, in 1906, but was implicated almost immediately in a shady episode revolving around a piece of zwieback, and had to leave town at the age of one. At sixteen Vincente, his blood fired by reports that Chicagoans were dancing the maxixe and the bunny-hug, set out to see for himself. Chicago was then a raw frontier town filled with prospectors and desperadoes like Walter Huston shooting at Gary Cooper through saloon doors. As Minnelli walked down the main street, his bandanna handkerchief tied to a peeled stick over his shoulder, munching a roll and whistling *The Lobster Is the Wise Guy, After All*, his eyes were like saucers. Little did he dream that one day he was to discover the secret of electricity and represent his country at the Court of St. James. Accosting a gamin whose dirty but humorous shoe-box marked him to be a bootblack, Vincente inquired politely where he might find lodgings for the night.

"Have yez any stamps?" inquired this personage.

"Stamps?" asked Vincente bewildered.

"Hully chee!" retorted the waif impatiently. "Kale—rhino—spondulicks—the long green! What's a matter—have yez bats in yer belfry?"

The intercession of honest old Bridget, the apple-woman of Trinity, whose name was a synonym for nausea in those parts, set the confused young traveler on the right path. He had barely turned the corner when a runaway horse, dragging a surrey containing a richly dressed young lady, dashed into view. After some speculation about the probable reward, Vincente threw himself at the foaming steed and was promptly trampled down. He spent several days moodily nursing his ribs, and finally driven to want by the scanty opportunities facing an untrained second-story worker, decided to humiliate himself and take a job.

As photographer's helper in a theatrical photo studio, the young man concluded that the moth-eaten costumes in which he posed various actors and actresses were atrocious, and he promptly started sketching. His employer's eyes still twinkle at the memory of one of these drawings, a sketch of the location of the office safe, which Vincente had negligently left in his smock. Soon after, the youthful draughtsman decided on a bold stroke. He went to the offices of Balaban & Katz, whose name had always haunted him with its suggestion of a roll on the kettle-drums, and suggested the idea of allowing him to design new costumes rather than renting old ones. Balaban & Katz at that time were the largest producers of stage shows for picture houses in the region, and they were thunderstruck at his audacity.

"But—but he's a mere tyro!" wailed Balaban when Katz told him of the offer.

"Whisht," returned Katz in the County Leitrim accent he loved to affect, "let's give him a try-o." In the uproar which followed, Minnelli found himself hired, and when Balaban & Katz took over the Paramount Theatre in New York, their protégé came along to take charge of the costume department.

New York! What magic the name evoked to the gangling youth in the worn old beaver as he followed a grinning red-cap out from the train shed of Grand Central! Flinging an oath at the expectant blackamoor, Vincente hailed a passing brioche and ordered the jehu to show him the sights. His eyes fairly bulged from their sockets at Chinatown with its huddled slaves of the poppy, the Brevoort with Richard Harding Davis falling down its front steps, and all the myriad wonders of the city. But soon the beaver on his head was stirring restlessly, slapping its flat tail on the nape of Vincente's neck, and it was time to appease the inner man. The pair dined famously off several birches in Central Park, and then, curled up in a hollow tree, lay watching the sparkling lights and wondering what adventures the morrow would bring.

In a few weeks Minnelli was doing backgrounds as well as costumes, but the spicy novels of Paul de Kock and Restif de la Bretonne had begun to make him yearn for Paris. On the verge of sailing to study painting at the feet of Claude Monet—a school had opened there a short time before—Minnelli was asked to design *The Dubarry* for Grace Moore. The opportunity of designing *The Du-*

barry for Grace Moore would probably never come to him twice in his life, and he decided to accept. For the next four years, he evolved a stage show a week for the Music Hall, and then, bored with idleness, designed the settings for *Life Begins at 8:40, At Home Abroad, The Ziegfeld Follies*, and *The Show Is On*. The latter attracted the attention of a little coalition of dreamers and visionaries named Paramount Pictures, and today Minnelli is one of Hollywood's most promising young directors.

There is a saying in Hollywood that when Vincente Minnelli is working on a picture you had better hide the women and children in the cellar and stay in bed with your hat on. "The Ohio Cyclone," as he is never called, observes a rigid routine. On rising, he scrubs his face free of the India ink, Chinese white, and water color of the day before. Then he chops up a few blotters and rolls them between his fingers till they disappear. Now he is ready for his milk bath. The huge black bathtub of vitreous milk-chocolate, his most cherished possession, is filled with thirty gallons of steaming Grade A. As he lolls back in the tub, Minnelli's mind becomes a beehive of ideas. Several efficient secretaries, who work for nothing merely to be near him, take down the acid retorts, thumbnail vignettes, pithy saws, and biting sarcasms which fall from his lips. These by-products are relayed to a corps of typists who bind and ship them to a firm of publishers, who in turn bind and ship them back. Meanwhile Minnelli busies himself making toy boats of the letters he receives from feminine admirers and sends them sailing away on a puff of fragrant Turkish. If a letter from some pathetic little seamstress or love-starved housewife should happen to intrigue him, he has one of the secretaries send her a photograph of himself in a characteristic pose. However, what with the Post Office Department's complaints, the photographs have fallen off to a minimum lately. And so the days go by, and before you know it, there are the twenty-four sheets advertising a new movie directed by Vincente Minnelli.

Of his private life, I know very little. I understand that he has become immensely wealthy, inordinately sought-after, and unbelievably unaffected. I count my spoons and my sisters every time he leaves my house. He has never once offered to repay me for my German silver watch-fob. But the first time I saw the settings and costumes he did for "The Steamboat Whistle" in *At Home Abroad*, I knew that all accounts were squared between us. I owe that boy *plenty*.

AVOCADO,
OR THE FUTURE OF EATING

(Note found in an empty stomach off Santa Barbara)

One day not long ago in Los Angeles I found myself, banderillas in hand, facing the horns of a dilemma. I had gone into a Corn Exchange bank to exchange some corn and had fallen into conversation with the manager. He was very affable and insisted I inspect the assets of the branch, which included, among other things, the teeth Bryant Washburn had used in his film career. Issuing into the hot sunlight of the street, I was dismayed to find that it was time for lunch, and since I had forgotten to bring along a bag of pemmican, I would have to eat in Los Angeles—a fairly exact definition of the term "the kiss of death." I looked around me. On my left I could obtain a duplexburger and a Giant Malted Milk Too Thick For a Straw; on my right the feature was barbecued pork fritters and orangeade. Unnerved, I stopped a passing street Arab and courteously inquired where I might find a cheap but clean eating house. Phil the Fiddler (for it was he) directed my steps to a pharmacy bearing the legend "Best Drug Stores, Inc." Merely for the record, I dined off an avocado sandwich on whole wheat and a lime rickey, and flunked my basal-metabolism test later that afternoon. I don't pretend to blame the management for my physical shortcomings; all I want them to do is laugh off their menu, a copy of which I seem to have before me.

In general, "Soda Fountain Suggestions" (Best Drug

Stores, Inc.) is an attractively printed job in two colors (three if you count the gravy), and though it can hardly hope to rival the success of *Gone with the Wind*, I suppose there is an audience which will welcome it. The salads and three-decker sandwiches are treated with a certain gaiety and quaint charm which recall *Alice of Old Vincennes*. The banana splits and hot-and-cold Ovaltines are handled with a glib humor in the text, which is more than I can say for the way they are handled behind the fountain. The day I was there, a simply appalling oath escaped the lips of one of the dispensers when he dropped some fudge on his shoe. The authors have included a very disarming foreword short enough to quote in its entirety: "It is our earnest desire to fulfill the name that we have chosen for our chain, THE BEST. We can only accomplish this by serving you best. Any criticisms or suggestions will be appreciated by the management." Only a churl would decline so graceful a gambit. *Messieurs, en garde!*

Specifically, gentlemen, my criticism concerns that cocky little summary of yours at the bottom of the menu. "BEST Soda Fountains," you proclaim flatly, "are BEST because: the ice creams contain no 'fillers' (starch, albumen, etc.); the syrups are made from cane sugar and real fruits; the coffee is a special blend made the modern Silex way with a specially filtered water," and so forth. Lest some of the younger boys in the troop think the millennium has come to the City of Our Lady, Queen of the Angels, what are the facts?

In the first place, you needn't think you can woo me

with any such tinsel as "the ice creams contain no 'fillers' (starch, albumen, etc.)." One thing I'll have in my ice cream or it's no dice—and that's fillers. I don't even insist on ice cream as long as I can stuff myself with fillers. You heap my plate with albumen and starch (any kind, even laundry starch) and stand clear. Call me a piggy if you want to, but I just can't get *enough* of that starch.

Quite honestly, your statement that the syrups "are made from cane sugar and real fruits" surprised me. If that's a boast, I must say it's a pretty hollow one. It might interest you to know that back in 1917 the Allied High Command specified *beet* sugar and *false* fruits in all syrups purchased by its commissary department. Didn't know that, did you? Probably too busy evading the draft at the time. Well, you just ask any biochemist his recommendation on sugars, as I did recently; you'll get the same terse answer: beet sugar and false fruits. I have this cousin of mine who is a perfect wiz at chemistry—really astonishing marks for a boy of nineteen in high school—and no matter what you ask him, he'll give you the same answer: beet sugar and false fruits. Frankly, the family's getting a little worried about it; they have to keep Benny chained to a ring in the floor most of the time.

Furthermore, it's useless to try to creep into my heart with any blandishments like "the coffee is a special blend made the modern Silex way with a specially filtered water." Filtering Los Angeles water robs it of its many nourishing ingredients, not the least of which is chow mein. It is an interesting fact, known to anybody who has ever been interned in that city or its suburbs, that the water possesses a rich content of subgum almond chow mein, Cantonese style, and one or two cases have even been reported where traces of peanut candy and lichee nuts were found. The assertion of a friend of mine that he once saw an Irish houseboy come out of a water faucet, of course, must be regarded as apocryphal. The Irish are a wiry little people, but they are not as wiry as all that. Nor are they ready as yet for the self-government which my distinguished opponents, the gentlemen of the affirmative, claim they should have. And so, honorable judges and ladies and gentlemen, we of the negative conclude that the Irish should not be given their independence because (1) we need them for a coaling station, (2) there is a high percentage of illiteracy, and (3) if we do, Ireland will soon be snatching up Guam—or "chewing Guam," so to speak. I thank you.

YOU SHOULD LIVE SO, WALDEN POND

Up the rolling ridge of Giggles Hill, a mile back from the Pennsylvania bank of the Delaware River, stands a modest stone house, pretty much as it stood during the last century. It is approached through a majestic avenue of large yellow signboards, placed there at ruinous expense and with no conviction whatever that he who runs will read. Beginning gently enough with the silky admonition "Fortified Area—Stay Off," the tone changes abruptly to a sinister "Communicable Diseases—Proceed at Your Own Risk." Should this prove inadequate, and it always does, the next two hundred feet are devoted to some choice billingsgate culled from Restoration plays, calculated to make a mule skinner flush to the roots of his hair. Unfortunately, since very few mule skinners pass that way, and those mostly bald, the effect is negligible, and by the time you top the rise beyond the persimmon trees, the signs culminate on a note of sheer hopelessness in a pair of 24-sheet billboards reading "Country Life: A Mockery" and "Solitude, My Foot."

Naturally enough I have been called everything from an old crosspatch to a modern Timothy Dexter of Newburyport. Indeed, whenever I drive my gig into the county seat for a pound of wire brads, of which I am inordinately fond, a troop of small boys invariably forms at my heels with taunts of "Oh, you modern Timothy Dexter of Newburyport!" So if I take the stand now in my own defense, it is only because Thoreau has had it long enough. Privacy in the country? Don't make me laugh, I've got a split personality.

Back in 1932, just before That Man came in and destroyed business confidence by reopening the banks, I belonged to a little group of profound thinkers who spent their evenings doing embroidery. The embroidery was on the theme, "If you have a small piece of dirt somewhere, you can always raise enough to keep you going." There was also a corollary which specified, "Nobody bothers you in the country. You can sleep as late as you like." Well, Sal's in a brothel, Pat's in jail, and I'm the one to tell the tale. I raised enough to keep myself going, all right, but my stomach never really became adjusted to ferns and hot water. Now I eat and drink whatever I like and sleep like a top—till shortly before dawn. Then the parade begins.

It is usually headed by a snaggle-toothed old bit player overpicturesquely made up as a hired man, who follows a well-worn routine. After sneaking around the house a few times to set the dogs in an uproar, he stations himself beneath my bedroom window and bawls out some obscene farrago, which presumably is a request for instructions about the chores. Properly keyed up on several brandies and armed with a pony, I can feel my way through Pennsylvania German dialect, but pluck me out of a sound slumber and I present a pitiable sight. Experience has taught me that to keep the respect of this man, whom I have never seen after five o'clock in the morning, I must pretend to give the matter deep thought. So for the next five minutes we both remain en *tableau*: he with an oily grin on his face, as though butter wouldn't melt in his mouth (he has even held up lumps of unmelted butter to me on occasion), and the young master swaying against the window, eyes closed and forefinger to temple in an attitude of profound concentration. In the end I give the fellow carte blanche and reel back to my crib, only to discover later, on arising again, that he has chopped down all the Chinese elms I planted last fall. Who pays the man to do this type of work I have no idea, unless it can be the War Office in Tokio.

Hardly am I back in the Taj Mahal, surrounded by Madeleine Carroll and five hundred million billion trillion dollars, when the masons, carpenters and assorted technicians arrive, minus tools but with plenty of noisemakers and confetti. After a brief warmup, which includes morris dancing on the green and feats of strength, one of their number, who is either eighteen feet high or uses a ladder, leans in at my window for a series of those highly complex questions you love to wake up to: "Hey, Mister, does the bushing fit over or under the flange on the cam?" or "Shall we put the differential on the housing or whitelead the gaskets? You haven't got a pound of sixpenny nails in there, have you?" Ignoring with considerable hauteur the implication that I am the sort of man who sleeps with sixpenny nails, I now rise and stand up in a clothes closet until time for breakfast.

Belowstairs, preparations have gone forward briskly to welcome the laird to his morning meal. Compared to my dining room, the floor of the Stock Exchange is a cloistered dell. The family motto seems to be "Let's tell him

now, he'll only find out anyway." Bubbling with infec-
tious laughter, the staff greets me with the news that the
hot-water system has gone to hell and rabbits have been
at the lettuce. Gramps, a lovable old white-haired charac-
:er who fought with Meade at Shiloh—he and Meade just
never got along—has been up since six, making his usual
inspection of the premises, and things look pretty black.
A large bird, cousin to the giant condor of the Andes, has
mysteriously wedged itself into the chimney during the
night; it might be cheaper to tear down the whole kitchen
wing while we're about it. None of the lespedeza he
planted yesterday is up yet, and the old gentleman
shouldn't wonder if they sold him last year's seed. With
the orange juice and coffee scarcely more than a hot ball
in my throat, instant decisions are now in order regarding
the dinner menu. What about roast-beef hash with gravy
and browned potatoes? Or a few salmon croquettes followed by boiled beef with horseradish and capers? Yes,
but don't put so much flour in the sauce. Well, you try
and cook with that oven. Nothing wrong with the oven;
we just bought it. Nothing wrong with the oven? *Didn't
we tell you?* This morning, just as Freda went to light the
burner. . . .

  83 ROLLING ACRES—Quaint old stone house—completely
restored—summer kitchen, guest house—historic maple shade
—orchard, never-failing creek, artesian well—30 acres in timber
—huge bank barn stabling 21 head—poultry houses, garage,
workshop, all farm implements—owner will exchange for
9 × 6 city apt. above 15th fl.—must have air shaft and no
view—apply immediately.

SWING OUT, SWEET CHARIOT

A few days ago I happened into my newsdealer's for ten cents' worth of licorice whips and the autumn issue of *Spindrift*, a rather advanced quarterly review in which I had been following an exciting serial called "Mysticism in the Rationalist Cosmogony, or John Dewey Rides Again." In the previous number, the cattle rustlers (post-Hegelian dogma) had trapped Professor Dewey in an abandoned mine shaft (Jamesian pragmatism) and had ignited the fuse leading to a keg of dynamite (neo-Newtonian empiricism). Naturally, I was simmering with impatience to learn how the Morningside Kid would escape from this fix, and I lost no time getting back to my rooms in the Middle Temple and stuffing my crusty old brier with shag. The gesture turned out to be singularly appropriate, for I shortly discovered that my newsdealer had made a mistake in his excitement and that I would have to spend the evening with a journal called *The Jitterbug*.

The Jitterbug is a febrile paper published bimonthly by the Lex Publications, Inc., of 381 Fourth Avenue, devoted to the activities of alligators, hepcats and *exaltés* of swing everywhere. These activities, which consist in hurling one another violently about to popular music, riding astride one another, and generally casting out devils, are portrayed in ten or fifteen pages of photographs and cartoons that need no explanation. What will bear a little exegesis, however, is the text of the half-dozen short

246

stories and articles. Were it not for the glossary of swing terms thoughtfully supplied by the management at the very outset, the magazine might as well be couched in Chinook. It may not concern anybody vitally that a "Scobo queen" is a girl jitterbug, that "frisking the whiskers" is warming up, that a "zeal girl" is a hot girl dancer, or that a "wheat bender" is one who plays sweet music instead of swing, but if you expect to translate such stories as "Jazz Beau," "Riffin' on the Range," and "Noodling with Love" without the aid of a trot, you are one hepcat indeed.

The qualifications of a working jitterbug are succinctly set forth in the national organizations' membership blank, which appears on page 21. It reads:

This is to certify that ——— is a jiving, hot-hosing Jitterbug, a member of the Community of Hep-Cats, and as such entitled to beat it out whenever the music swings out high, wide, and gutbucket.

The characters involved in the aforementioned stories are all that and more. For example, Cal Leonard, the protagonist of "Jazz Beau," is described as "a pair of Mack Truck shoulders, a grinning mouth, and wild, flame-blue eyes." I suppose there was a body linking these goodies together, but the pace is so staccato that the author neglects to mention it. Debby Waite, of "Noodling with Love," on the other hand, has body and to spare, judging from the following tender blueprint:

Her thick, curly red-gold hair was kind of piled up on top and around her head, and it made a shining halo that framed

247

the white oval of her face. Those sultry lips of hers were red and glistening under the lights, and her gray eyes sparkled like hot rhythm. Debby's figure was never anything to be missed, but in the two years since I'd seen her, several delectable curves I remembered had ripened. And the dress she was wearing wasn't calculated to hide that fact. Its full chiffon skirt tantalized by its seeming transparency, and it clung to the soft roundness of her hips with loving closeness. The waist was high and tight, and above that rose two shields that fitted snugly over the proud mounds of her swelling breasts.

In fine, a Schrafft's Luxuro ice-cream sundae come to life; and, as though I were not overheated enough already, the author has to pile Pelion on Ossa by telling me this glorious blob of girlhood was educated at Bennington. Look, dear, I wouldn't care if she had quit school in the sixth grade.

The plots of the short stories in my copy of *Jitterbug* are fairly basic: Scobo queen meets hep-cat, they find mutual release in barrelhouse or gut-bucket, and eventually, on the winsome revelation that one or the other is heir to half a million rugs, shag, peck, and paw their way to the altar. "Jazz Beau" may serve as a clinical example. A young lady describing herself as a Taxi-Tessie or wriggle-wren employed at the Roselane Ballroom is lured into a Broadway movie theatre by the harmonies of one Biggie Barnett and his band:

I heard the wail of a wah-wah pump, the staccatoed stutter of skins. . . . My heart began to thump and swell with the fever of rhythm. I giggled out loud. Crazily, I slid to a stop at the aisle, in the theatre proper, scanned the seats. Full. I felt my breasts tremor angrily.

This mysterious physiological reaction, no doubt experienced by every woman at the sight of an S.R.O. sign, yields to a state bordering on epilepsy when the band really starts giving:

I began to sway in my seat. My lashes fluttered. My head bobbed in time with the red hot ride rhythm. Jittersauce began to burn up my bloodstream.

At this point, as the *cognoscenti* begin stomping and trucking freely about in a delirium of pleasure, the surrealist owner of the Mack Truck shoulders, grinning mouth, and wild flame-blue eyes enters the proceedings:

"Lookee," the big guy whispered, "I've *got* to get out in that aisle and whip my dogs! Do we team up? A big gazabo like me is gonna look awfully silly getting off a solo!"

Hesitating a split second lest her suppliant turn out to be a geep, or wolf, Miss Prim surrenders to his emotional plea and joins the gavotte:

While those cats up on the stage clambaked like nobody's business, my partner and I really cut that rug. . . . All I was conscious of was the driving syncopation and lift of agony pipes, the noodling of the brass section, as barrelhouse blasts whipped my slender legs and weaving hips into a rhythmic frenzy. We did the Suzy-Q. We shagged and pecked.

His appetite whetted by this preliminary workout, Cal declares his intention of making a night of it. "My sox are hell-hot and I've got to hop till I wear holes in my soles to cool them off," he avers, and his escort, whose disposition is no less elastic than her frame, readily assents. "We strutted and stuffed to burning boogie-woogie, stayed in the groove until we were both beat right down," she whispers shyly to her diary. Thereupon, in a passage as salty as any you will find in the Kamasutra, the gymnasts take leave of each other until the following evening, when Cal "came swaggering into Roselane looking like a color-page from *Esquire*." Maybe the engraver's hand slipped, but the last color-page from *Esquire* I saw was slightly off register and showed a junior executive with a flesh-colored suit and a pale-blue herringbone face. Had Cal worn something of the sort, however, he could hardly have caused a greater sensation. In a trice the other hostesses cluster excitedly about his affinity, asking whether she knows Cal's father is a millionaire motor magnate in Detroit. The little lady loves Cal for his floy floy alone, and her disillusion and heartbreak are such that she is almost thirty seconds recovering from the shock. "You don't think of those things when you're with a guy who's slowly driving you screwball with love," she observes with icy disdain. Perhaps not, puss, but it certainly wouldn't do any harm to look the old gent up in Dun & Bradstreet—now, would it? I mean just for the heck of it.

Follows an interval of courtship in which, fanned by love and jive, Cal's passion mounts to a crescendo. He becomes a nightly visitor to Roselane, buying rolls of dance tickets and "paying out a small fortune" (probably upward of three dollars in a single evening) to keep off poachers. A drunken geep who engages our miss in the Portland fancy finds himself "bounced off two walls after

Cal hit him." But Cal's importunate proposals of marriage are met with the only answer a high-grade heroine of fiction can give: "Everyone would think I was wedding you for your papa's shekels. You'd even think it yourself, after the romance wore off." The chilling presentiment of a loveless union between two graying jitterbugs retired to the bench and soaking their feet in a pail of Tiz nevertheless fails to dissuade Cal: "He begged. He pleaded. He made love with words [the last desperate throw of the dice] like Red Norvo swings 'Reverie.'" Yet all to no avail, for in a scene of renunciation worthy of Tolstoy (not Leo Tolstoy; a man I know named Charlie Tolstoy), the narrator gives the mitten to "the one and only guy who had played on my heart strings like a bass-man picks at a belly fiddle."

And now, in a Garrison finish, Cal calls forth the tenacity and cunning that have made his father a caution in the automotive industry. He retains two geeps to enter Roselane, trip up his inamorata while dancing with her, and so humiliate her that she is forced to resign her post. This incomprehensibly restores the social equation between the lovers and sends them on a honeymoon wherein they "shagged and trucked and Suzy-Q-ed and hugged and kissed." The narrative concludes, "Anyhow, when two alligators get together and love sets in, you've got something."

I'll say I have, sister. Did you ever hear tell of migraine?

SECOND-CLASS MATTER

What has gone before: Poultney Groin, disillusioned and middle-aged playboy, member of Manhattan's "upper crust," tires of Simone Dravnik, beauteous model whom he has been protecting. Womanlike, stung to the quick, she stares into her hand-mirror in her lavishly appointed apartment on Park Avenue and asks herself the age-old question: *Finished your dinner? Now it's acid's turn to dine! These small cavities filled with decomposed food morsels rapidly hatch bacteria. In a few hours your formerly healthy system is a mass of putrefaction. Ask Dr. Fritz P. Tanzpalast of the German Deaconess Hospital in Chicago. Or ask Mr. Fred Dahlgren of Norfolk, Virginia. Dog mah cats, folks, jes' give me mah spoon vittles, mah side-meat an' yams, an' dat little blue tin of Edgeworth, sho sho.* Down the dusty Chisholm trail into Abilene rode taciturn Spit Weaver, his lean brown face an enigma and his six-gun swinging idly from the pommel of Moisshe, the wonder horse. *I'm curryin' my dogs in a pail of hot H_2O when the ball-and-chain ankles in beamin'. I get the bulge on her both ways from the whistle. Listen, sister, I snarls, Spike McGinnity'll be a pushover for the Kid's meathooks. He'll be kissin' the canvas in two frames. So take a powder. You're slugnutty, grates she, how you gonna do it? Just bend the old auditory apparatus, meanin' ear, I warbles. Women of America, all you worried fatties, simply apply my marvelous Thinno treatment to that sagging, foolish bosom of yours and in* ten minutes you'll be as svelte as a Fifth Avenue model—svelter, by Christ. Vy svelter in the city's heat when poised, self-possessed cosmopolitans rub elbows in the Salon Mixte of the S.S. "Getroffen"? Mingle with courtly diplomats, scintillating stars of stage and screen, and world-famous bon vivants in the spacious, airy playrooms of this floating week-end! Shoot clay ducks in the privacy of your cabin! Roach-ridden, pockmarked, hog-fat, land-poor, nigger-rich, penny-wise and pound-foolish genuine Breton stewards attend to your every want! Beginning next month: Edith Waterhouse Prattfogle's dynamic novel of human destinies against the brilliant background of a Hawaiian volcano. A tapestry shot through and through with the vivid plumage of pleasure-mad sybarites. A flaming pageant of a forbidden love. White man ... brown girl ... caught in the volcanic drama of life ... on the sun-drenched shores of a magic isle ... where blood runs hot and the heart is free and man holds in fierce embrace the alluring image of elemental woman as the jealous God in the Mountain of Fire sunders the earth and splits the skies and hurls the sea to a bottomless pit because she broke the savage Taboo! Shape your nose the new scientific way with this new device discovered by leading European chemists. Freckles, pimples, wrinkles, blackheads, enlarged pores, pits, pots, pans, abrasions, painter's colic, trachoma, treachery, and trainman's headache all disappear before this invigorating compound. Dog of a Christian unbeliever, know then that in all Samarkand dwells none as lovely as gazelle-eyed Vashtar. Even the lotus petal fades before her modest demeanor, and when she walks abroad veiled in her yashmak, foolhardly indeed is he who would dare gainsay her. But in the crooked Street of Ten Thousand Lanterns wily Ah Gow fingered a jade-encrusted fly worth a prince's ransom and kept his own counsel. Verily is it written that the fool has a hundred tongues but the wise man will mother a clucking hen with soft speeches. Parsley Braddon of the violet eyes and the storm-tossed curls lounged moodily in her chaise-longue atop Gotham's loftiest skyscraper. Her exquisitely modeled shoulders shivered disgustedly at the thought of Southampton in August. *Feh! Ptoo!* If only Roddy Lathrop and Mimi Lubliner would call for her in their yellow speedster. To feel the giddy onrush of wind in her hair as she sped down the Merrick Road—free, free! *Lots o' folks figger they're sassiety fellers becuz they own a claw-hammer coat. Pussonally, I'd be a dern sight happier a-whittlin' chaws off'n my old plug o' Mechanics Delight. And Mr. Burns, however homely his philosophy, is right. This little box of Tasty Chocolate candy . . . collapsible, easily cleaned, fits into any orifice . . . will blow the be-jesus out of your lazy colon. Clean house! Clear the decks! Clear the courtroom! Open your bowel and let the sunlight in!* It was glamour that put highlights in her hair, glamour that made him throw back his shoulders like a young Lochinvar come riding out of the West. Young they were, absurdly young . . . brave, defiant of the world, lazing the days away. All both of them wanted was a little nook. Foolish, tender, quixotic, impulsive, generous to a fault, they called me Aunt Vi, albeit I was scarcely three years their senior. At times their innocence and gay bravado brought a lump to my throat. Take the lump of margarine, whip well with a skein of gray worsted, roll well in breadcrumbs till your skin gets that tingly feeling, and then ask these six questions of your Church toilet seat. My husband was touchy, morose, flatulent. He would leave for his office in the morning, throw himself at his typewriter, and practically tear the clothes off her. I consulted a specialist and together we examined the fine, saw-toothed edges of the tissue under the microscope. Sure enough . . . they were snails. We hesitated at first but after the garçon assured us, we tried them and found them delicious. We also visited La Reine Pedauque, Weber's, the Tomb of Napoleon, the House of All Nations, and many other spots of the City of Light. All in all the trip cost us two hundred and five dollars, including tips. Well, dear Betty, "nuf sed" for tonight and I certainly must say that the Furness-Withy Lines are all a body could want in the way of economical, pleasant travel. Oh, yes, and I mustn't neglect to tell you that two seventeen-thousand-ton, steam-heated liners leave every Tuesday and Saturday for Haifa and Smyrna from Pier 89. To Tracy Hand, a formal figure with elegant hands erect by the rosewood spinet, his cravat a white patch of arrogance below his dark, alien face, the futility of life in Salem was a fact, a proved quantity. Poppaea couldn't, he knew, feel the resentment, inevitably, which he had been storing up inside him. The notes died in the twilight and he turned carefully, almost stiffly, toward the gun-room. However brittle his role in the succession of frivolities which he tolerated in this house, the memory of Lily Jastrow's laughter followed him. *Frankly, we're Knox-label-conscious . . . and why not? We'd be dull young moderns not to realize that* après tout *Knox gelatin has that certain* je ne sais quoi . . . *That how you say* élan . . . *That mysterious "spreadable" quality possessed only by this zesty old cheddar dusted lightly over wheaty little Thinsies.* You there, Uncle Mose, you black rascal, whuffo' ain't you done bring in de cunn'l's fatback 'n' co'n-pone? Faix an' begorra, Ah's been savoring de delicious odor ob Chase and Sanborn's date-marked coffee, befo' de Lawd! Well, Mose, I certainly can't blame you for that, but where did you get it? Why, Bascom's, just above Forty-fourth Street, you know. Which explains how Mr. Demosthenes P. Johnson, late Grand Sachem of the Affiliated Sons of the Imperial Order of the Setting Star, happened to be walking down F Street in the Ethiopian quarter of Birmingham, Alabama. He had just passed the tonsorial parlors of T. Agamemnon Snowball (Motto: We shave you, you save yourself) when he was hailed by a familiar voice. Turning, he descried the beaming lineaments of none other than Pericles Q. Shoat, late vice-president in charge of production of the Abyssinian Motion-Picture Studios. *You American mothers, in those intimate little heart-to-heart talks with your daughters, what about this question of shashlik (the medical name for soiled stomach)? You like to think of yourself as a sister to Mary Ellen, not as a mother, and yet you are allowing the fluff to accumulate in her navel and store up illnesses for later years. You must be a pretty flea-bitten son-of-a-bitch, dash it all! But that's only part of our service! We, the makers of*

Roylcord-Bounceaway tires, the tire habit of a nation, the tire with the triple suction grips, the double reinforced shock-absorbing cushion-impact, and that modern innovation in tire-engineering, floating shoulder pressure, have posted a bond with 184 of America's leading insurance companies. If any tire bearing our name blows out in less than six hundred thousand miles of use, you can take it and shove it into the nearest post-office and receive postpaid an absolutely new one in exchange! Remember it's shish kebab (your doctor's name for sensitive epidermic tissue) which shortens your shave-life! Boy, you haven't felt shave-ease on your old shave-surface till you've discovered Shav-Komfy, the shave-secret of the Aztecs! Evening was a bright lasso drawing the sun's red ball behind the ridge when Virgil Spafford stopped the Ford outside Gedney's. Man-fashion, he made as if to pass April, laughing there in the little circle of onhangers. She was a bright lasso drawing awkward young men down from the farms. Virgil snorted; her hand fluttered from his coat, and he entered Gedney's. Gedney's, the bright lasso which drew the main street of Shoreham into a hard, angular knot, was empty, partially through having burned down the previous month, partially because old man Gedney had never set foot in Shoreham. Brazilian peons, humming their native songs, picked the coffee which flavors this new and startling confection; from the snowy summits of the Andes came long-fibred llama wools to give it body; and from our own Pennsylvania coal-fields comes the delicious gritty anthracite dust which is making this obscene little candy the lunch-substitute of millions. A mischievous breeze molded the outline of her figure against the dunes. Cap'n Eben Mushmouth chuckled to himself and relit his pipe. Sairy Ann would have plenty to say about this new arrival in Hyannis. *Forty Fathom mackerel, scales glistening with the still-fresh brine of the Georges Bank, bursting with impatience to leap into your frying-pan and treat your palate to a real old-fashioned tummy-fest! In galvanized-iron hermetically sealed pails direct from our cleaning sheds in Gloucester to your doorstep!* And now, dear reader, a final word from Mr. Editor Mans. We have scoured the fiction market to set before you *Three Million Tiny Sweat Glands Functioning* in that vibrant panorama of tomorrow so that *Your Sensitive Bowel Muscles Can* react to the inevitable realization that only by enrichment and guidance *plus a soothing depilatory* can America face its problems confidently, unafraid, *well-groomed, mouth-happy, breaking the hair off at the roots without undue stench. Okay, Miss America!*

WHOLLY
CLEANING AND DYEING

I have been kept so busy by Uncle Fagin filching ladies' handkerchiefs that it was only yesterday I realized the spring and summer issues of *The Cleaning and Dyeing World* and *The National Cleaner and Dyer* are out again, bursting with the sort of surprises we have come to expect from *The Cleaning and Dyeing World* and *The National Cleaner and Dyer*. It is all very well to be blasé about it, Mr. Man of the World, as you loll in your glittering brioche along Rotten Row and idly suck liqueur candies, but every hot-blooded aficionado of dry-cleaning will hurl his cap into the air at the news. Any statistician will tell you that there are literally thousands of people in the United States today interested in every phase of dry-cleaning, which is a good handy reason for avoiding statisticians. As for me, I could hardly wait until I got my teeth into the new numbers of these breezy little magazines, and I was not disappointed. They taste even better than the January and February issues, and that faint flavor of peppermint in the binding was nothing short of an inspiration. We fried a couple of the rotogravure pages for lunch and they had a crisp, crunchy quality like fried smelts. You have to be rather careful chewing them, as the binding is full of sharp little staples, but the half-tones are simply delicious and altogether both magazines are fine eating.

Unfortunately, reading them is an entirely different proposition. I have waded through some dull wordage in my day, but if there is anything as trying as an article on mothproofing a vest, I prefer to remain in the dark about it. To make matters worse, I have a little fixation about moths which I am able to control most of the time, but half-way through the article a pair of those filmy gray types suddenly fluttered out of the magazine itself and tried to settle on my face. Now you know that isn't any way to hold a reader spellbound. The janitor said he never heard a man scream like that.

The Cleaning and Dyeing World and The National Cleaner and Dyer, however, now and then forget themselves sufficiently to let slip a trade secret or two. For instance, I always wondered who was in charge of scorching my gray flannels and spattering them with ink at the dry-cleaning plant, and how much he had to pay for the concession. It now turns out that this work is only entrusted to experts, who are even paid to do it by their vengeful bosses. Surely hatred of the customer could go no further. The National Cleaner and Dyer for May, under "Positions Wanted" advertises: "Expert Fancy Spotter, all around man, 23 years practical experience best plants. Box 509." ("Best pants" is obviously what the fool means—he'll never get a job that way.) An expert silk spotter, who sounds as though he could raise hell with crinkly crepes, is also available for special vandalism on ladies' garments, care of Box 510. Another valuable bit of technical information is the note in the May Cleaning and Dyeing World which states "The plural of 'tailor's goose' is not 'geese' but 'gooses'." The next time you enter your tailor's shop, try this out on him and see what it gets you. It got me a rather nasty blow on the knuckles with a flat-iron which I am still trying to laugh off.

But it is in the Question-and-Answer Department of *The Cleaning and Dyeing World* that the unshriven dry-cleaner, hungry for absolution, unlocks his lips and pours out his follies. In this Sargasso Sea drift some strange hulks; witness the appalling confession which appeared in the May issue:

"A brand new white velvet dress was put in the pressing machine the first thing in the morning. A few drops of condensed steam containing rust dripped out of the buck. While it was still wet we applied pre-spotter, thinking that it would absorb the water, and put it into our synthetic solvent unit. After the run the spot of rust remained.

"Next we applied a rust-removing preparation, but that did not remove it. After it was thoroughly rinsed out we used potassium permanganate followed by sodium bisulphite and oxalic acid. When that dried out there was a large brown spot where the $KMNO_4$ had been. Can you advise us how to remove the brown spot?—G. D., Pa."

In Heaven's name, what in the world is wrong with a nice brown blob of potassium permanganate on the front of a white velvet dress? Schiaparelli would pivot her whole winter collection around an idea like that; she'd make up a line of evening jewelry out of Bunsen burners to go with it that would knock your eye out. But if G.D. is really afraid of a *crise* on the part of his client, there is only one solution. The dress should be wrapped in a back number of *The Cleaning and Dyeing World*, taken to Grand Central, and checked at the East Parcel Room.

The dry-cleaner then mails the receipt to the customer and boards the night train to Montreal. I learned this trick from Samuel Leibowitz, who tells me that you cannot extradite a dry-cleaner, much less remain in the same room with one.

There is a slightly hesitant air about Mr. A. C. W. of Fla., as he straggles up to the mourner's bench with the following horrid little case history in the April *Cleaning and Dyeing World:*

"We have a pair of brown flannel pants that we dry-cleaned in the usual way, then wet-cleaned them. They came out with grayish-white splotches all over them. We wet-cleaned and dry-cleaned again to no advantage. We have never before had any trouble like this. Can you tell us something to remedy this trouble?"

Trouble is what you make it, my boy, and it's no use going around with a let-down nose over a few white splotches. If you can't bully the customer into thinking that he is seeing specks before his eyes, you are not the stuff dry-cleaners are made of. Just keep chewing on that dead cigar stump and saying "G'wan, you little weasel, why don't you have your eyes examined?" while the customer yells himself hoarse. If he threatens to sue, remind him calmly that your uncle is a judge in the Appellate Division. Should he scream back that *his* uncle is a judge in the Appellate Division too, that constitutes a tie and must be played off at a later date.

The fine old tradition of tough-sinewed, hard-bitten dry-cleaners has passed and in its stead has appeared a race of white-livered milksops. Typical of this namby-pamby attitude is the spineless letter of W. L. A., Okla., in the March *Cleaning and Dyeing World:*

"I am a small town Dry Cleaner with only eight years of experience. However, I am quite a student and go to places of learning when I can afford it. I attended the Short Course at Ames, Iowa, in June, 1930. I shall not be satisfied till I have graduated from the National School at Silver Spring, Maryland.

"Under separate cover I am sending you a specimen from a green dress that so far makes me feel more of a novice than I am. I cleaned this dress and returned it myself without a spot on it. Two days after the customer called us telling us there were lots of stiff places on this dress. She says she did not wear it and blames us for these spots.

"I could not figure out what the spots were unless they could be paint. I sponged out with dilute alcohol, then dry cleaned in Stoddard Solvent, without removing the spots. I would not try any other chemicals, being ignorant of the kind of stain it was, so I am asking you to let me know what they are."

I may be all haywire, W. L. A., but from where I am sitting those spots look suspiciously like dried froth from the customer's lips. That little lady is raging mad, and no amount of honeyed words or complimentary coathangers engraved with your name is going to mollify her. Your one chance is contained in the advertisement the Page Engineering Company of Syracuse inserted in the March issue of *Cleaning and Dyeing World:*

"*Hat Machine Only $142.50*—Can be connected to pressing machine. Simple to operate. Just plug in and run."

And whatever you do, brother, keep on running.

WELL, ROLL ME
IN A TURKISH TOWEL!

If the gentlemen in the upper half of the amphitheatre will be so good as to move down—there, that's better. The patient is a well-developed white male of thirty-nine in moderate shock. His skin is moist and cool, temperature 99.1 F., pulse 130, blood pressure 78/60. The complaint is localized in the head and ears, the general conformation of which is that of an early Greek amphora. Note that the eyeballs are rolling skyward and that the lips are puckered as though they had bitten into a quince. A routine pocket analysis performed upon admission, however, yielded no quinces, which suggests that the trouble is seated elsewhere. The abdomen is noticeably spastic and when percussed reacts with a series of delicious little tremors. The case history, while scanty, reveals that the subject was recently exposed to a hang tag packed by the Irwill Knitwear Corporation in one of its ladies' sweaters. A mild psychic trauma is indicated, with increasing pressure, and syncope around the corner as sure as God made little green apples.

Now don't get me wrong, men. I'm perfectly willing to lie here under this sheet and be tickled by a pretty probationer if it's going to advance the cause of science, but confidentially, you're barking up the wrong tree. There's nothing the matter with me; I'm just suffering from a little sweater tag, and if you could let me rest here a second I'll be tiptop in no time. I still can't understand how it happened. Yesterday I was hunting through the

264

guest closet for a paper box when I ran across one containing a pink-and-gray card, on the order of a dance program, suspended from a loop of fuchsia-colored twine. It showed a young woman attired in a sweater bearing the words "Jane Irwill' across her *poitrine* and a quaint biography of the garment, as follows: "Years ago I was just a little jacket for babies. In the Gay Nineties I went to school and college, growing rough and tough and developing a turtle neck. The women adopted me for sports next, but soon I was appearing everywhere all day long. Now I am quite grown up and go out in the evening, too." Sponging a bead of moisture from my upper lip with a delicate wisp of cambric, I turned the card over, preparatory to grinding it under my heel. On the flap was a dainty mandate entitled "Order of the Bath": "Please wash me in lukewarm water with Ivory Flakes. Squeeze the suds through me carefully—never scrub or twist me—rinse me carefully, and roll me in a Turkish towel. Then lay me flat, stretch me to my original shape and dry me in the shade away from all heat. Thank you. Jane Irwill."

You're welcome, sweetheart. I had always supposed that merchandising reached its apogee in the Lux advertisement which portrayed two articles of lingerie discussing their wearers' effluvia, for all the world like rival stamp collectors, but this latest conceit deserves some special decoration, like the Croix de Mal-de-Mer, second class, with moist palms. The implication that only feminine apparel is vocal, however, is pure sexual chauvinism and eminently unfair, The next speaker, an elderly button-down, or polo shirt, has been known to me personally for a number of years. It is currently retired to the country, from which it emerges periodically in a succession of farewell tours, like the late Adelina Patti, but between you and me and the compost, its race is well-nigh run. Frankly, I can think of a number of better things to do than to sit here and listen to a frayed old shirt shoot off its face, but since we've come this far there's no turning back.

"Well, folks, I am duss an old Brooks Brothers shirt and to look at me you would nevcr dwcam of all the sights I've seen. I dess I will dwop this confounded prattle and slip into something more comfy. Well, folks, it just seems like yesterday that I first saw him staring into the showcase at me. He and the other man were both sort of red in the face, as if they had had too much to drink at lunch. He was easily the best-looking thing I had ever seen— great, broad shoulders almost a foot across, an adorable little belly like a cantaloupe, and the cunningest ferret eyes, which kept darting around on watch for the credit manager.

" 'Hot zeugma!' I heard him murmur to his friend, motioning toward me. 'How'd you like to go home with *that*?' His friend whispered something back and they both burst into a coarse guffaw. Naturally, I made out I hadn't overheard, but my heart was going like a trip hammer and all I could think of was 'Please, Lord, please, make him take me. I'll work and I'll slave for him, only don't let him get away.' Then I suddenly realized how hopeless the whole thing was. We were worlds apart; I was just a common little domestic oxford weave from the wrong side of the Garment Center and he had everything—position and money and breeding. I found out later that he had nothing but a rusty old charge account, but at that moment it wouldn't have mattered. A second later I almost fainted dead away; he was saying something to the salesman and pointing in at me. He had the most provocative, blurry way of speaking—not exactly a lisp, more of a harelip effect. You felt that half the time he didn't know what he was going to say next, and it gave him a kind of a loose-leaf air that was utterly charming.

" 'Now for crisakes remember to shorten the sleeves this time,' he was barking at the salesman. 'Every goddam shirt you send me, the cuffs hang down to the knees. What do you think I am, an orangutan?'

" 'Yes, sir,' the salesman said hastily, making a note on his pad.

" 'Oh, I am, am I?' he shouted. 'Did you hear that, Leo? This four-eyed bastard called me an orangutan. Here, help me over the counter. Put up your dukes, there! I'm going to start swinging in a minute!'

" 'Now take it easy, *tovarisch*,' his friend pleaded, edging him toward the door. 'It's pretty warm in here. Maybe that last brandy and soda—'

" 'Oh, so I'm drunk, eh?' he snarled, flinging aside his friend's arm. 'Just an old broken-down barfly, hah? But I'm good enough to sponge drinks off, aren't I? Thass a fair-weather friend for you. All right for you, Jocko.' With that he collapsed on the floor and burst into tears. 'I never got the breaks,' he sobbed. 'Every man's hand is against me. Beat me. Stone me.' It finally took the floor-walker and two clerks from the glove division to get him into a cab. The last I saw of him, his head was pillowed on his friend's shoulder and he was yodelling 'Auprès de Ma Blonde.'

"Bright and early the next morning, I was waiting outside his apartment, all done up in tissue and quivering with excitement. Through the cardboard box I heard a doorbell and guttural voices.

" 'Who's that for, the lush in forty-two?'

" 'Yeah, is he home?'

" 'He's home all right. They brung him back in a pail from the Copacabana. That's him groanin' now.' Soon fingers started fumbling with my wrappings and I was face to face with him. He seemed less boisterous, more mature; in fact, he had aged fifteen years during the night. His hands were trembling, his forehead burned with fever, and a tracery of delicate purple veins stood out in bas-relief on his nose. He goggled at me for a moment, and then, with a bestial oath, flung me across the room, demolishing a piece of bric-a-brac. Humiliated, stung by his contempt, I cried out in pain. His face slowly turned ashen and his sparse hairs rose en brosse with fright.

" 'Who said that?' he quavered, his eyes shifting about fearfully. 'There's somebody in this room!'

" 'You rotter,' I choked. 'You thing.' His jaw dropped and his tongue clacked against his teeth like castanets.

" 'Help!' he screamed suddenly. 'It talked! A talking shirt!' He struck out blindly at me, went off balance, and rolled over me, kicking and gouging. One of the pins in my tail caught in his pajamas and his frenzy redoubled. 'Get it off me!' he squealed. 'I'm stabbed. Call a priest!'

The door opened and a woman in a dressing gown entered, leisurely sipping a cup of coffee. She stood coldly surveying the poor wretch clawing the carpet.

" 'Well, Sweets,' she said tonelessly, 'are you ready for bed or are you going to play bean bag under the radiator all day?' After a short, unequal tussle with his wife and the maid, he was borne off whimpering to his couch. As the maid threw me into the hamper with an obscure West Indian malediction, his ululations were just beginning to subside.

"He wore me only once, several months afterwards, when he was tricked into lunching with a soiled dove in a sordid *boîte* in the East Sixties. Toward the end of the afternoon, his vis-à-vis, overcome by his magnetism, seized him in a grip of steel and began smothering his face with kisses. In all justice to him, he fought off the dastardly attack with every fibre of his being, but a smear of lipstick on my collar proved to be his undoing. In the post-mortem which ensued at home, his wife drew first claret and I was banished to the country. I occasionally see him down there, whenever the furnace needs cleaning or he tries to simulate poverty in order to get an extension at the bank. He still thinks he's a playboy, although his chins have outgrown my neckband twice over and his paunch flutters like a custard if he merely laces his shoes. I'm as young as I ever was. That's a hell of a lot more than I can say for him."

PHYSICIAN, STEEL THYSELF

Do you happen to know how many tassels a Restoration coxcomb wore at the knee? Or the kind of chafing dish a bunch of Skidmore girls would have used in a dormitory revel in 1911? Or the exact method of quarrying peat out of a bog at the time of the Irish Corn Laws? In fact, do you know anything at all that nobody else knows or, for that matter, gives a damn about? If you do, then sit tight, because one of these days you're going to Hollywood as a technical supervisor on a million-dollar movie. You may be a bore to your own family, but you're worth your weight in piastres to the picture business.

Yes, Hollywood dearly loves a technical expert, however recondite or esoteric his field. It is a pretty picayune film that cannot afford at least one of them; sometimes they well-nigh outnumber the actors. The Sherlock Holmes series, for instance, employs three servants on a full-time basis—one who has made a lifelong study of the décor at 221-B Baker Street, a second deeply versed in the great detective's psychology and mannerisms, and a third who spots anachronisms in the script which may distress Holmesians, like penicillin and the atomic bomb. An ideal existence, you might think, and yet there have been exceptions. I knew a White Russian artillery officer at M-G-M, imported at bloodcurdling expense from Algeria as adviser on a romance of the Foreign Legion, who languished for two years in an oubliette under the Music

Department. Over the noon yoghurt, his voice trembled as he spoke of his yearning to return to Russia, where they were waiting to shoot him, but the director of "Blistered Bugles" felt him indispensable. At last he departed, with close to forty thousand rutabagas in his money belt, a broken man. His sole contribution was that he had succeeded in having "pouf" altered to "sacré bloo." Another expert I met during the same epoch was a jovial, gnarled little party named Settembrini, conceded to be the foremost wrought-iron craftsman in the country. He had been flown three thousand miles to authenticate several flambeaux shown briefly in a night shot of Versailles. We subsequently chanced to be on the same train going East, and except for the fact that he wore a gold derby and was lighting his cigar with a first-mortgage bond, he seemed untouched. "Fine place," he commented, flicking ashes into the corsage of a blonde he had brought along for the purpose. "Sunshine, pretty girls, grapefruit ten for a quarter." I asked him whether the flambeaux had met the test. "One hundred per cent," he replied, "but they threw 'em out. In the scene where Marie Antoinette comes down the steps, a lackey holds a flashlight so she don't trip over her feet."

The latest group of specialists to be smiled upon by the cinema industry, it would appear, are the psychoanalysts. The vogue of psychological films started by *Lady in the Dark* has resulted in flush times for the profession, and anyone who can tell a frazzled id from a father fixation had better be booted and spurred for an impending summons to the Coast. The credit title of

Spellbound, Alfred Hitchcock's recent thriller, for example, carried the acknowledgment "Psychiatric sequences supervised by Dr. May Romm," and Sidney Skolsky, reporting on a picture called *Obsessed* (formerly *One Man's Secret* and before that *One Woman's Secret*), states, "Joan Crawford is huddling with an eminent psychiatrist who will psych her forthcoming role in *The Secret* for her." A psychiatrist suddenly pitchforked into Hollywood, the ultimate nightmare, must feel rather like a small boy let loose in a toy store, but I wonder how long he can maintain a spirit of strict scientific objectivity. The ensuing vignette, a hasty attempt to adumbrate this new trend, is purely fanciful. There are, naturally, no such places as the Brown Derby, Vine Street, and Hollywood Boulevard, and if there should turn out to be, I couldn't be sorrier.

SHERMAN WORMSER, M.D., PHD., came out of the Hollywood Plaza Hotel, somewhat lethargic after a heavy Sunday brunch, and paused indecisively on the sidewalk. The idea of taking a walk, which had seemed so inspired a moment ago in his room, now depressed him immeasurably. To the south, Vine Street stretched away interminably—unending blocks of bankrupt night clubs, used-car lots, open-air markets, and bazaars full of unpainted furniture and garden pottery. To the north, it rose abruptly in a steep hill crowned by a cluster of funeral homes and massage parlors in tan stucco. Over all of it hung a warm miasma vaguely suggestive of a steam laundry. Sherman moved aimlessly toward the boulevard and paused for a brief self-inventory in the window of the Broadway-Hollywood department store.

Most of Dr. Wormser's patients in New York, accustomed to his neat morning coat and pencil-striped trousers, would have had some difficulty in recognizing their father confessor at the moment. He wore a pea-green play suit with deep, flaring lapels, tailored of rough, towel-like material, arbitrarily checked and striated in front but mysteriously turned to suède in back. Over a gauzy, salmon-colored polo shirt he had knotted a yellow foulard handkerchief in a bow reminiscent of George Primrose's Minstrels, and on his head was sportily perched an Alpinist's hat modelled after those worn by the tyrant Gessler. Eight weeks before, when he had arrived to check on the dream sequences of R.K.O.'s *Befuddled*, he would not have been caught dead in these vestments, but his sack suits had seemed so conspicuous that, chameleon-like, he soon developed a sense of protective coloration.

He had settled his hat at a jauntier angle and was turning away from the window when he became aware that a passer-by was staring fixedly at him. The man wore an off-white polo coat which hung open, its belt trailing on the pavement. Underneath were visible pleated lavender slacks and a monogrammed yachting jacket trimmed with brass buttons. The face under the scarlet beret was oddly familiar.

"I beg pardon," hesitated the stranger, "I think we—you're not Sherman Wormser, are you?" At the sound of his voice, Sherman's mouth opened in delight. He flung his arm about the man's shoulder's.

"Why Randy Kalbfus, you old son of a gun!" he crowed. "Two years ago! The Mental Hygiene Convention in Cleveland!"

"Bull's-eye," chuckled Kalbfus. "I thought it was you, but— well, you look different, somehow."

"Why—er—I used to have a Vandyke." Wormser felt his cheeks growing pink. "I shaved it off out here. The studio, you know. Say, you had one, too, for that matter. What became of yours?"

"Same thing," Kalbfus admitted sheepishly. "My producer said it was corny. He's got a block about psychiatrists' wearing goatees."

"Yes, involuntary goatee rejection," nodded Wormser. "Stekel speaks of it. Well, well. I heard you were in town. Where you working?"

"Over at Twentieth. I'm straightening out a couple of traumas in Delirious."

"You don't say!" Despite himself, Sherman's tone was faintly patronizing. "I turned down that assignment, you know. Didn't feel I could justify the symbolism of the scene where Don Ameche disembowels the horse."

"Oh, that's all out now," said Kalbfus amiably. "That was the early version."

"Well," said Sherman quickly, eager to retrieve himself, "it's the early version that catches the Wormser, what?" Kalbus laughed uproariously, less at the witticism than because this was the first time anyone had addressed him in three days.

"Look," he suggested, linking arms with Sherman, "let's hop over to the Bamboo Room and have a couple of Zombolas." On their way across to the Brown Derby, he explained the nature of the drink to Wormser, who was still a bit staid and Eastern in his choice of beverages. "It's just a tall glass of rum mixed with a jigger of gin, some camphor ice, and a twist of avocado," he said reassuringly.

"Isn't that a little potent?" asked Wormser dubiously.

"You're cooking with grass it's potent," returned his companion pertly, if inaccurately. "That's why they won't serve more than six to a customer." Seated in the cool darkness of the bar, with three Zombolas coursing through their vitals, the colleagues felt drawn to each other. No trace of professional hostility or envy lingered by the time they had finished reviewing the Cleveland convention, the rapacity of their fellow-practitioners, and their own staunch integrity.

"How do you like it out here, Randy?" Wormser inquired. "I get a slight sense of confusion. Perhaps I'm not adjusted yet."

"You're inhibited," said Kalbfus, signalling the waiter to repeat. "You won't let yourself go. Infantile denial of your environment."

"I know," said Wormser plaintively, "but a few weeks ago I saw Jack Benny in a sleigh on Sunset Boulevard— with real reindeer. And last night an old hermit in a pillowcase stopped me and claimed the world was coming to an end. When I objected, he sold me a box of figs."

"You'll get used to it," the other replied. "I've been

275

here five months, and to me it's God's country. I never eat oranges, but hell, can you imagine three dozen for a quarter?"

"I guess you're right," admitted Wormser. "Where are you staying?"

"At the Sunburst Auto Motel on Cahuenga," said Kalbfus, draining his glass. "I'm sharing a room with two extra girls from Paramount."

"Oh, I'm sorry. I—I didn't know you and Mrs. Kalbfus were separated."

"Don't be archaic. She's living there, too." Kalbfus snapped his fingers at the waiter. "Once in a while I fall into the wrong bed, but Beryl's made her emotional adjustment; she's carrying on with a Greek in Malibu. Interesting sublimation of libido under stress, isn't it? I'm doing a paper on it." Wormser raised his hand ineffectually to ward off the fifth Zombola, but Kalbfus would not be overborne.

"None of that," he said sharply. "Come on, drink up. Yes, sir, it's a great town, but I'll tell you something Sherm. We're in the wrong end of this business. Original stories—that's the caper." He looked around and lowered his voice. "I'll let you in on a secret, if you promise not to blab. I've been collaborating with the head barber over at Fox, and we've got a ten-strike. It's about a simple, unaffected manicurist who inherits fifty million smackers."

"A fantasy, eh?" Wormser pondered. "That's a good idea."

"What the hell do you mean, fantasy?" demanded
276

Kalbfus heatedly. "It happens every day. Wait till you hear the twisteroo, though. This babe, who has everything—houses, yachts, cars, three men in love with her—suddenly turns around and gives back the dough."

"Why?" asked Wormser, sensing that he was expected to.

"Well, we haven't worked that out yet," said Kalbfus confidentially. "Probably a subconscious wealth phobia. Anyway, Zanuck's offered us a hundred and thirty G's for it, and it isn't even on paper."

"Holy cow!" breathed Wormser. "What'll you do with all that money?"

"I've got my eye on a place in Beverly," Kalbfus confessed. "It's only eighteen rooms, but a jewel box—indoor plunge, indoor rifle range, the whole place is indoors. Even the barbecue."

"That can't be," protested Wormser. "The barbecue's always outdoors."

"Not this one," beamed Kalbfus. "That's what makes it so unusual. Then, of course, I'll have to give Beryl her settlement when the divorce comes through."

"You—you just said everything was fine between you," faltered Wormser.

"Oh, sure, but I've really outgrown her," shrugged Kalbfus. "Listen, old man, I wouldn't want this to get into the columns. You see, I'm going to marry Ingrid Bergman."

A strange, tingling numbness, like that induced by novocain, spread downward from the tips of Wormser's ears. "I didn't know you knew her," he murmured.

277

"I don't," said Kalbfus, "but I saw her the other night at the Mocambo, and she gave me a look that meant only one thing." He laughed and swallowed his sixth Zombola. "It's understandable, in a way. She must have known instinctively."

"Known what?" Wormser's eyes, trained to withstand the unusual, stood out in high relief.

"Oh, just that I happen to be the strongest man in the world," said Kalbfus modestly. He rose, drew a deep breath, and picked up the table. "Watch," he ordered, and flung it crisply across the bar. Two pyramids of bottles dissolved and crashed to the floor, taking with them a Filipino bus-boy and several hundred cocktail glasses. Before the fixtures had ceased quivering, a task force of bartenders and waiters was spearing down on Kalbfus. There was an obscure interval of scuffling, during which Wormser unaccountably found himself creeping about on all fours and being kicked by a fat lady. Then the shouts and recriminations blurred, and suddenly he felt the harsh impact of the pavement. In a parking lot, eons later, the mist cleared and he was seated on the running board of a sedan, palpating a robin's egg on his jaw. Kalbfus, his face puffier than he last remembered it, was shakily imploring him to forgive and dine at his motel. Wormser slowly shook his head.

"No, thanks." Though his tongue was a bolt of flannel, Sherman strove to give his words dignity. "I like you, Kalbfuth, but you're a little unthtable." Then he got to his feet, bowed formally, and went into the Pig'n Whistle for an atomburger and a frosted mango.

278

PALE HANDS I LOATHE

To paraphrase Omar the Tentmaker slightly (oh, come on, it can't hurt to paraphrase Omar the Tentmaker just a teeny bit), I often wonder what the editors of the *Woman's Home Companion* buy one half so precious as the thing they sell. The thing they sell me, specifically, is nepenthe; whenever my salt loses its savor, I know I can find heartsease in those shiny, optimistic pages, whether in the latest prize-winning recipe for macaroni-and-cheese timbales or some ingenious method of canning babies for winter use. More than a companion, yet less than a mistress, it is my home away from home, my wife away from wife, my dream girl of the magazine world, *Woman's Home Companion*, I adore you.

It was, therefore, with a sense of disquietude that I detected in the February issue a certain monotony I had never noticed before. The infants gurgled on as darling and cuddlesome as ever; the meat loaves and veal birds were, if anything, even more economical than they had been in the January number. But instead of the rich pastiche of lingerie and soufflés I expected in the advertising columns, I found only a series of variations on a single theme—the care of Milady's hands. For page after page, the manufacturers of innumerable unguents and lotions endlessly conjugated the tragedy of rough, chapped hands. "My poor hands!" snuffled the housewife in the advertisement for Pacquins Hand Cream. "They made me feel like an OLD TURKEY," and to dramatize the full poignancy of her affliction, the victim was shown in a second phase transmuted into an aged, weather-beaten turkey. "I use HINDS—that HONEY of a lotion," crowed another housewife, hefting a coal scuttle and celebrating you-know-whose Honey and Almond Cream. Jergens Lotion took a rather more romantic approach and portrayed a handsome officer nibbling at his fiancée's fingers, while Campana Cream Balm presented a pair of war sweethearts over the hushed caption: "It was one of those golden, delirious moments . . . impulsively his hands sought mine . . . and together we welcomed the first tender touch of romance." Toushay, the "Beforehand" Lotion, demonstrated its versatility with four mysterious vignettes of a young lady stroking a kitten, washing her undies, simpering at some convalescent soldiers, and finally nuzzling her warrior, home on leave.

It was our humdrum old friend, Ivory Soap, though, that put its competitors to shame and set my ordinarily robust stomach palpitating like a plate of junket. It depicted a personable matron fondly discussing her mate over the telephone with some undisclosed critic, as follows: "Hard-boiled? *Him*? Don't you believe it! What hard-boiled husband would tramp halfway across town to get that special coffee cake I adore so for Sunday breakfast? Would a really tough guy take time out now and then—like in the middle of his favorite pecan pie— just to grab my hands and kiss them? Yes—gruff as he seems to others, in private, he fairly raves about my pretty hands!"

I have searched diligently through Freud, Jung, Brill,

Menninger, and Zilboorg for a clue to this interesting form of hand worship, but can find no analogous instance, either with or without pecans. I suspect, however, that if we pull on a pair of waders and whip the husband's stream of consciousness, using the kind of tackle Mr. Joyce employed on Leopold Bloom, we may catch a few shiners. Here, then, is the interior monologue of Lester Wagenhals, incisive, hard-bitten office manager of the Puissant Valve & Flange Corporation, as he sits at his desk about five o'clock of a mid-winter afternoon:

"Funny taste in my mouth. Must be that noodle ring I had for lunch. Urr-r-gh. Good thing I keep extra bag of pecans in desk drawer. Careful now. Secretary might walk in. Nasty little snooper. Lovely hands, though. Wish I could bite them. Better not. Can't afford scandal. Just one quick bite? No. Complications. Lose my head. One bite leads to another. Road to hell paved with soft white hands. Good thought there. Wasting my time in business. Should have been a poet. Plenty of mazuma in poetry if a man went at it efficiently. Snug studio in Greenwich Village. High jinks. Red wine and red-hot mammas. Turn your damper down. Life in the old boy yet. Man is as young as he feels. Lick my weight in wildcats.

"Ought to finish this letter to Abernethy about those bushings. *Yours of the 14 inst. to hand.* There I go again. Hands all over the place. Try again. *Cannot see our way clear to take consignment off your hands.* No good. Sleep on it. Best not to rush into these things, anyway. Past five o'clock. Eunice waiting. Comb my hair and wash my. Steady. Lean against filing cabinet a second. Buzzing in the temples. Never should have eaten that noodle ring. Scores die as police blame poisoned noodle ring. FBI uncovers secret noodle ring in Midwest. Wait. Wipe perspiration off forehead. Reception clerk might blab to J.B. Can hear them talking right now. Wagenhals slowing up. Nice old duffer but can't keep abreast of modern methods. Organization full of dead ducks. Terminating as of the first. One month's salary in recognition of the service you have ren. Appreciate if you will explain system to Mr. Samish, the dirty sneak you have been protecting right in your own office. Law of the jungle, dog eat dog, root or die. Alert, capable executive desires wide-awake connection. Sorry, position just filled. Sorry, looking for aggressive younger man. Will call you if anything. Compelled to foreclose. Beg to advise that insurance has lapsed. Some bank with facilities for handling smaller accounts like yours. Eunice taking in washing. Rough laundry hands. No more pecan pies. Bellevue. Oh, my God.

"Buck up now. Walk slowly past their desks. Bunch of clock-watchers. Lazy, no-good riffraff. Give them the old glare. Snap their heads off. Carlson at the water-cooler. O.K., Carlson, your goose is cooked. *Running Horse* sticking out of Bender's pocket. Knock them off tonight. No, tomorrow will do. Much too kindhearted for my own good.

"There. Lucky my getting this elevator car. Cute brunette, that operator. Pity she wears gloves. Bet she has superb hands. Ask her for a peek? No, might misunderstand. Invite her out for cocktail some time. Pretend I'm big advertising man. Need model with special type of fingers to pose for national account. Strictly business, no monkey-shines. Careful not to frighten her off. Discuss various types of hands. Purely scientific spirit. Index of character, they say. Yours, for example. Cold hands, warm heart. Paternal smile, old enough to be your father. Casually mention wife. Hopeless invalid. Haven't had anything to do with her for years. Pile it on. Man needs pair of soft white hands to come home to. Home is where the hands are. Just the same, better use pseudonym. Never can tell about these dolls. Lead you on and then the shakedown. Man in Cleveland who fell for a lady elevator starter. Turned out to be head of Midwest blackmail ring. Stripped him of his last noodle. Urr-r-gh. That taste again.

"Fresh air feels good. Where did I say meet Eunice? Astor? Plaza? No, Biltmore lobby. Walk along Sixth. Interesting shops around here. Secrets of the Polynesian Love Cults. Figure Drawing for Second-Year Sadists. Nice prints in this art store. French kid wearing porcelain casserole on head. Pretty racy if you could read the text. Plaster-of-Paris Venus. Ditto foot and hand. Chap who designed that never saw woman's hand. Do better with my eyes closed. Outrage the way they mulct unsuspecting public. Law against it. Letter to the *Times*. Couldn't palm it off on yours truly. Palm off hand. Neat phrase. Work it in.

"Green light. Cross now. Too late, catch it next corner. Automat coming up. Just time for fast pecan bun before Eunice. No, mustn't. Sure to smell it on my breath. Use cloves. Only an evasion. Can't hurt to look in window, though. Row on row of delicious, crackly. Who's to tell? Never know when some friend of Eunice. Oh, rats. Only live once. Long time dead. Long time no pecan bun. Look up and down first. Hurry.

"Easy now. People looking at you. Stop trembling. Debonair stroll. Man of the world dropping in for late-afternoon snack. Nothing out of the ordinary. Draw hot chocolate first. Enough. Don't bother with saucer. Now the pastry. More pecans on the twist than the buns. Count them. Don't be a sheep. Get your money's worth. Look out, manager watching you. Three nickels, quickly. Something wrong. Door is stuck. Hit it. Pound it. There, it's opening. So is the panel in back. Woman's hand reaching through. Exquisite, tapering fingers redolent of Ivory Soap. One little kiss. Opportunity of a lifetime. Grab them, you fool! Yum yum yum yum yum. . . . Capital. Now all I have to do is talk my way out of this."

INSERT FLAP "A"
AND THROW AWAY

One stifling summer afternoon last August, in the attic of a tiny stone house in Pennsylvania, I made a most interesting discovery: the shortest, cheapest method of inducing a nervous breakdown ever perfected. In this technique (eventually adopted by the psychology department of Duke University, which will adopt anything), the subject is placed in a sharply sloping attic heated to 340°F. and given a mothproof closet known as the Jiffy-Cloz to assemble. The Jiffy-Cloz, procurable at any department store or neighborhood insane asylum, consists of half a dozen gigantic sheets of red cardboard, two plywood doors, a clothes rack, and a packet of staples. With these is included a set of instructions mimeographed in pale-violet ink, fruity with phrases like "Pass Section F through Slot AA, taking care not to fold tabs behind washers (see Fig. 9)." The cardboard is so processed that as the subject struggles convulsively to force the staple through, it suddenly buckles, plunging the staple deep into his thumb. He thereupon springs up with a dolorous cry and smites his knob (Section K) on the rafters (RR). As a final demonic touch, the Jiffy-Cloz people cunningly omit four of the staples necessary to finish the job, so that after indescribable purgatory, the best the subject can possibly achieve is a sleazy, capricious structure which would reduce any self-respecting moth to helpless laughter. The cumulative frustration, the tropical heat, and the soft, ghostly chuckling of the moths are calculated to unseat the strongest mentality.

In a period of rapid technological change, however, it was inevitable that a method as cumbersome as the Jiffy-Cloz would be superseded. It was superseded at exactly nine-thirty Christmas morning by a device called the Self-Running 10-Inch Scale-Model Delivery-Truck Kit Powered by Magic Motor, costing twenty-nine cents. About nine on that particular morning, I was spread-eagled on my bed, indulging in my favorite sport of mouth-breathing, when a cork fired from a child's air gun mysteriously lodged in my throat. The pellet proved awkward for a while, but I finally ejected it by flailing the little marksman (and his sister, for good measure) until their welkins rang, and sauntered in to breakfast. Before I could choke down a healing fruit juice, my consort, a tall, regal creature indistinguishable from Cornelia, the Mother of the Gracchi, except that her foot was entangled in a roller skate, swept in. She extended a large, unmistakable box covered with diagrams.

"Now don't start making excuses," she whined. "It's just a simple cardboard toy. The directions are on the back—"

"Look, dear," I interrupted, rising hurriedly and pulling on my overcoat, "it clean slipped my mind. I'm supposed to take a lesson in crosshatching at Zim's School of Cartooning today."

"On Christmas?" she asked suspiciously.

"Yes, it's the only time they could fit me in," I countered glibly. "This is the big week for crosshatching, you know, between Christmas and New Year's."

"Do you think you ought to go in your pajamas?" she asked.

"Oh, that's O.K.," I smiled. "We often work in our pajamas up at Zim's. Well, goodbye now. If I'm not home by Thursday, you'll find a cold snack in the safe-deposit box." My subterfuge, unluckily, went for naught, and in a trice I was sprawled on the nursery floor, surrounded by two lambkins and ninety-eight segments of the Self-Running 10-Inch Scale-Model Delivery-Truck Construction Kit.

The theory of the kit was simplicity itself, easily intelligible to Kettering of General Motors, Professor Millikan, or any first-rate physicist. Taking as my starting point the only sentence I could comprehend, "Fold down on all lines marked 'fold down;' fold up on all lines marked 'fold up,'" I set the children to work and myself folded up with an album of views of Chili Williams. In a few moments, my skin was suffused with a delightful tingling sensation and I was ready for the second phase, lightly referred to in the directions as "Preparing the Spring Motor Unit." As nearly as I could determine after twenty minutes of mumbling, the Magic Motor ("No Electricity —No Batteries—Nothing to Wind—Motor Never Wears Out") was an accordion-pleated affair operating by torsion, attached to the axles. "It is necessary," said the text, "to cut a slight notch in each of the axles with a knife (see Fig. C.). To find the exact place to cut this notch, lay one of the axles over diagram at bottom of page."

"Well, now we're getting some place!" I boomed, with a false gusto that deceived nobody. "Here, Buster, run in

287

and get Daddy a knife."

"I dowanna," quavered the boy, backing away. "You always cut yourself at this stage." I gave the wee fellow an indulgent pat on the head that flattened it slightly, to teach him civility, and commandeered a long, serrated bread knife from the kitchen. "Now watch me closely, children," I ordered. "We place the axle on the diagram as in Fig. C, applying a strong downward pressure on the knife handle at all times." The axle must have been a factory second, because an instant later I was in the bathroom grinding my teeth in agony and attempting to stanch the flow of blood. Ultimately, I succeeded in contriving a rough bandage and slipped back into the nursery without awaking the children's suspicions. An agreeable surprise awaited me. Displaying a mechanical aptitude clearly inherited from their sire, the rascals had put together the chassis of the delivery truck.

"Very good indeed," I complimented (naturally, one has to exaggerate praise to develop a child's self-confidence). "Let's see—what's the next step? Ah, yes. 'Lock into box shape by inserting tabs C, D, E, F, G, H, J, K, and L into slots C, D, E, F, G, H, J, K, and L. Ends of front axle should be pushed through holes A and B.' " While marshalling the indicated parts in their proper order, I emphasized to my rapt listeners the necessity of patience and perseverance. "Haste makes waste, you know," I reminded them. "Rome wasn't built in a day. Remember, your daddy isn't always going to be here to show you."

"Where are you going to be?" they demanded.

"In the movies, if I can arrange it," I snarled. Poising tabs C, D, E, F, G, H, J, K, and L in one hand and the corresponding slots in the other, I essayed a union of the two, but in vain. The moment I made one set fast and tackled another, tab and slot would part company, thumbing their noses at me. Although the children were too immature to understand, I saw in a flash where the trouble lay. Some idiotic employee at the factory had punched out the wrong design, probably out of sheer spite. So that was his game, eh? I set my lips in a grim line and, throwing one hundred and fifty-seven pounds of fighting fat into the effort, pounded the component parts into a homogeneous mass.

"There," I said with a gasp, "that's close enough. Now then, who wants candy? One, two, three—everybody off to the candy store!"

"We wanna finish the delivery truck!" they wailed. "Mummy, he won't let us finish the delivery truck!" Threats, cajolery, bribes were of no avail. In their jungle code, a twenty-nine-cent gewgaw bulked larger than a parent's love. Realizing that I was dealing with a pair of monomaniacs, I determined to show them who was master and wildly began locking the cardboard units helter-skelter, without any regard for the directions. When sections refused to fit, I gouged them with my nails and forced them together, cackling shrilly. The side panels collapsed; with a bestial oath, I drove a safety pin through them and lashed them to the roof. I used paper clips, bobby pins, anything I could lay my hands on. My fingers fairly flew and my breath whistled in my throat. "You want a delivery truck, do you?" I panted. "All right, I'll show you!" As merciful blackness closed in, I was on my hands and knees, bunting the infernal thing along with my nose and whinnying, "Roll, confound you, roll!"

"Absolute quiet," a carefully modulated voice was saying, "and fifteen of the white tablets every four hours." I opened my eyes carefully in the darkened room. Dimly I picked out a knifelike character actor in a Vandyke beard and pencil-striped pants folding a stethoscope into his bag. "Yes," he added thoughtfully, "if we play our cards right, this ought to be a long, expensive recovery." From far away, I could hear my wife's voice bravely trying to control her anxiety.

"What if he becomes restless, Doctor?"

"Get him a detective story," returned the leech. "Or better still, a nice, soothing picture puzzle—something he can do with his hands."

FAREWELL, MY LOVELY APPETIZER

Add Smorgasbits to your ought-to-know department, the newest of the three Betty Lee products. What in the world! Just small mouth-size pieces of herring and of pinkish tones. We crossed our heart and promised not to tell the secret of their tinting.—*Clementine Paddleford's food column in the Herald Tribune.*

The "Hush-Hush" Blouse. We're very hush-hush about his name, but the celebrated shirtmaker who did it for us is famous on two continents for blouses with details like those deep yoke folds, the wonderful shoulder pads, the shirtband bow!—*Russeks adv. in the Times.*

I came down the sixth-floor corridor of the Arbogast Building, past the World Wide Noodle Corporation, Zwinger & Rumsey, Accountants, and the Ace Secretarial Service, Mimeographing Our Specialty. The legend on the ground-glass panel next door said, "Atlas Detective Agency, Noonan & Driscoll," but Snapper Driscoll had retired two years before with a .38 slug between the shoulders, donated by a snowbird in Tacoma, and I owned what good will the firm had. I let myself into the crummy anteroom we kept to impress clients, growled good morning at Birdie Claflin.

"Well, you certainly look like something the cat dragged in," she said. She had a quick tongue. She also had eyes like dusty lapis lazuli, taffy hair, and a figure that did things to me. I kicked open the bottom drawer of her desk, let two inches of rye trickle down my craw, kissed Birdie square on her lush, red mouth, and set fire to a cigarette.

"I could go for you, sugar," I said slowly. Her face was veiled, watchful. I stared at her ears, liking the way they were joined to her head. There was something complete about them; you knew they were there for keeps. When you're a private eye, you want things to stay put.

"Any customers?"

"A woman by the name of Sigrid Bjornsterne said she'd be back. A looker."

"Swede?"

"She'd like you to think so."

I nodded toward the inner office to indicate that I was going in there, and went in there. I lay down on the davenport, took off my shoes, and bought myself a shot from the bottle I kept underneath. Four minutes later, an ash blonde with eyes the color of unset opals, in a Nettie Rosenstein basic black dress and a baum-marten stole, burst in. Her bosom was heaving and it looked even better that way. With a gasp she circled the desk, hunting for some place to hide, and then, spotting the wardrobe where I keep a change of bourbon, ran into it. I got up and wandered out into the anteroom. Birdie was deep in a crossword puzzle.

"See anyone come in here?"

"Nope." There was a thoughtful line between her brows. "Say, what's a five-letter word meaning 'trouble'?"

"Swede," I told her, and went back inside. I waited the length of time it would take a small, not very bright boy to recite *Ozymandias*, and, inching carefully along the wall, took a quick gander out the window. A thin galoot with stooping shoulders was being very busy reading a paper outside the Gristede store two blocks away. He hadn't been there an hour ago, but then, of course, neither had I. He wore a size seven dove-colored hat from Browning King, a tan Wilson Brothers shirt with pale-blue stripes, a J. Press foulard with a mixed red-and-white figure, dark blue Interwoven socks, and an unshined pair of ox-blood London Character shoes. I let a cigarette burn down between my fingers until it made a small red mark, and then I opened the wardrobe.

"Hi," the blonde said lazily. "You Mike Noonan?" I made a noise that could have been "Yes," and waited. She yawned. I thought things over, decided to play it safe. I yawned. She yawned back, then, settling into a corner of the wardrobe, went to sleep. I let another cigarette burn down until it made a second red mark beside the first one, and then I woke her up. She sank into a chair, crossing a pair of gams that tightened my throat as I peered under the desk at them.

"Mr. Noonan," she said, "you—you've got to help me."

"My few friends call me Mike," I said pleasantly.

"Mike." She rolled the syllable on her tongue. "I don't believe I've ever heard that name before. Irish?"

"Enough to know the difference between a gossoon and a bassoon."

"What *is* the difference?" she asked. I dummied up; I figured I wasn't giving anything away for free. Her eyes narrowed. I shifted my two hundred pounds slightly, lazily set fire to a finger, and watched it burn down. I could see she was admiring the interplay of muscles in my shoulders. There wasn't any extra fat on Mike Noonan, but I wasn't telling her that. I was playing it safe until I knew where we stood.

When she spoke again, it came with a rush. "Mr. Noonan, he thinks I'm trying to poison him. But I swear the herring was pink—I took it out of the jar myself. If I could only find out how they tinted it. I offered them money, but they wouldn't tell."

"Suppose you take it from the beginning," I suggested.

She drew a deep breath. "You've heard of the golden spintria of Hadrian?" I shook my head. "It's a tremendously valuable coin believed to have been given by the Emperor Hadrian to one of his proconsuls, Caius Vitellius. It disappeared about 150 A.D., and eventually passed into the possession of Hucbald the Fat. After the sack of Adrianople by the Turks, it was loaned by a man named Shapiro to the court physician, or hakim, of Abdul Mahmoud. Then it dropped out of sight for nearly five hundred years, until last August, when a dealer in second-hand books named Lloyd Thursday sold it to my husband."

"And now it's gone again," I finished.

"No," she said. "At least, it was lying on the dresser when I left, an hour ago." I leaned back, pretending to fumble a carbon out of the desk, and studied her legs again. This was going to be a lot more intricate than I had thought. Her voice got huskier. "Last night I brought home a jar of Smorgasbits for Walter's dinner. You know them?"

"Small mouth-size pieces of herring and of pinkish tones, aren't they?"

Her eyes darkened, lightened, got darker again. "How did you know?"

"I haven't been a private op nine years for nothing sister. Go on."

"I—I knew right away something was wrong when Walter screamed and upset his plate. I tried to tell him the herring was supposed to be pink, but he carried on like a madman. He's been suspicious of me since—well, ever since I made him take out that life insurance."

"What was the face amount of the policy?"

"A hundred thousand. But it carried a triple-indemnity clause in case he died by sea food. Mr. Noonan—Mike"— her tone caressed me—"I've got to win back his confidence. You could find out how they tinted that herring."

"What's in it for me?"

"Anything you want." The words were a whisper. I leaned over, poked open her handbag, counted off five grand.

"This'll hold me for a while," I said. "If I need any more, I'll beat my spoon on the high chair." She got up. "Oh, while I think of it, how does this golden spintria of yours tie in with the herring?"

"It doesn't," she said calmly. "I just threw it in for glamour." She trailed past me in a cloud of scent that retailed at ninety rugs the ounce. I caught her wrist, pulled her up to me.

"I go for girls named Sigrid with opal eyes," I said.

"Where'd you learn my name?"

"I haven't been a private snoop twelve years for nothing, sister."

"It was nine last time."

"It seemed like twelve till you came along." I held the clinch until a faint wisp of smoke curled out of her ears, pushed her through the door. Then I slipped a pint of rye into my stomach and a heater into my kick and went looking for a bookdealer named Lloyd Thursday. I knew he had no connection with the herring caper, but in my business you don't overlook anything.

The thin galoot outside Gristede's had taken a powder when I got there; that meant we were no longer playing girls' rules. I hired a hack to Wanamaker's, cut over to Third, walked up toward Fourteenth. At Twelfth a mink-faced jasper made up as a street cleaner tailed me for a block, drifted into a dairy restaurant. At Thirteenth somebody dropped a sour tomato out of a third-story window, missing me by inches. I doubled back to Wanamaker's, hopped a bus up Fifth to Madison Square, and switched to a cab down Fourth, where the second-hand bookshops elbow each other like dirty urchins.

A flabby hombre in a Joe Carbondale rope-knit sweater, whose jowl could have used a shave, quit giggling over the Heptameron long enough to tell me he was Lloyd Thursday. His shoebutton eyes became opaque when I asked to see any first editions or incunabula relative to the *Clupea harengus*, or common herring.

"You got the wrong pitch, copper," he snarled. "That stuff is hotter than Pee Wee Russell's clarinet."

"Maybe a sawbuck'll smarten you up," I said. I folded one to the size of a postage stamp, scratched my chin with it. "There's five yards around for anyone who knows why those Smörgasbits of Sigrid Bjornsterne's happened to be pink." His eyes got crafty.

"I might talk for a grand."

"Start dealing." He motioned toward the back. I took a step forward. A second later a Roman candle exploded inside my head and I went away from there. When I came to, I was on the floor with a lump on my sconce the size of a lapwing's egg and big Terry Tremaine of Homicide was bending over me.

"Someone sapped me," I said thickly. "His name was—"

"Webster," grunted Terry. He held up a dog-eared copy of Merriam's Unabridged. "You tripped on a loose board and this fell off a shelf on your think tank."

"Yeah?" I said skeptically. "Then where's Thursday?" He pointed to the fat man lying across a pile of erotica. "He passed out cold when he saw you cave." I covered up, let Terry figure it any way he wanted. I wasn't telling him what cards I held. I was playing it safe until I knew all the angles.

In a seedy pharmacy off Astor Place, a stale Armenian whose name might have been Vulgarian but wasn't dressed my head and started asking questions. I put my knee in his groin and he lost interest. Jerking my head toward the coffee urn, I spent a nickel and the next forty minutes doing some heavy thinking. Then I holed up in a phone booth and dialled a clerk I knew called Little Farvel in a delicatessen store on Amsterdam Avenue. It took a while to get the dope I wanted because the connection was bad and Little Farvel had been dead two years, but we Noonans don't let go easily.

By the time I worked back to the Arbogast Building, via the Weehawken ferry and the George Washington Bridge to cover my tracks, all the pieces were in place. Or so I thought up to the point she came out of the wardrobe holding me between the sights of her ice-blue automatic.

"Reach for the stratosphere, gumshoe." Sigrid Bjornsterne's voice was colder than Horace Greeley and Little Farvel put together, but her clothes were plenty calorific. She wore a forest-green suit of Hockanum woolens, a Knox Wayfarer, and baby crocodile pumps. It was her blouse, though, that made tiny red hairs stand up on my knuckles. Its deep yoke folds, shoulder pads, and shirtband bow could only have been designed by some master craftsman, some Cézanne of the shears.

"Well, Nosy Parker," she sneered, "so you found out how they tinted the herring."

"Sure—grenadine," I said easily. "You knew it all along. And you planned to add a few grains of oxylbutane-cheriphosphate, which turns the same shade of pink in solution, to your husband's portion, knowing it wouldn't show in the post-mortem. Then you'd collect the three hundred g's and join Harry Pestalozzi in Nogales till the heat died down. But you didn't count on me."

"You?" Mockery nicked her full-throated laugh. "What are you going to do about it?"

"This." I snaked the rug out from under her and she went down in a swirl of silken ankles. The bullet whined by me into the ceiling as I vaulted over the desk, pinioned her against the wardrobe.

"Mike." Suddenly all the hatred had drained away and her body yielded to mine. "Don't turn me in. You cared for me—once."

"It's no good, Sigrid. You'd only double-time me again."

"Try me."

"O.K. The shirtmaker who designed your blouse — what's his name?" A shudder of fear went over her; she averted her head. "He's famous on two continents. Come on Sigrid, they're your dice."

"I won't tell you. I can't. It's a secret between this— this department store and me."

"They wouldn't be loyal to you. They'd sell you out fast enough."

"Oh, Mike. vou mustn't. You don't know what you're asking."

"For the last time."

"Oh, sweetheart, don't you see?" Her eyes were tragic pools, a cenotaph to lost illusions. "I've got so little. Don't take that away from me. I—I'd never be able to hold up my head in Russeks again."

"Well, if that's the way you want to play it . . ." There was silence in the room, broken only by Sigrid's choked sob. Then, with a strangely empty feeling, I uncradled the phone and dialled Spring 7-3100.

For an hour after they took her away, I sat alone in the taupe-colored dusk, watching lights come on and a woman in the hotel opposite adjusting a garter. Then I treated my tonsils to five fingers of firewater, jammed on my hat, and made for the anteroom. Birdie was still scowling over her crossword puzzle. She looked up crookedly at me.

"Need me any more tonight?"

"No." I dropped a grand or two in her lap. "Here, buy yourself some stardust."

"Thanks, I've got my quota." For the first time I caught a shadow of pain behind her eyes. "Mike, would—would you tell me something?"

"As long as it isn't clean," I flipped to conceal my bitterness.

"What's an eight-letter word meaning 'sentimental'?"

"Flatfoot, darling," I said, and went out into the rain.

The Best of the World's Best Books
COMPLETE LIST OF TITLES IN
THE MODERN LIBRARY

For convenience in ordering use number at right of title

MISCELLANEOUS